Rivka and Chaya, 1941

For Mom, with all my love

CHAPTER ONE

A Lucky Start

Rivka, January 11, 1941

Chaya

Rivka was the second oldest of ten children. She knew all about babies, having been the "little mama" to eight younger brothers and sisters. But when she was 26 and her daughter Chaya was born, she witnessed something she'd only heard about in old wives' tales.

Chaya came into the world with the birth sac on her head like a little cap. "You know what this means?" said the midwife to Rivka, who marveled at the sight.

"Yes," Rivka said. She knew the folklore. This was a sign. It meant Chaya would be a lucky child.

As Chaya was handed to her, Rivka gazed at her daughter's face for the first time. A sense of calm washed over her. Chaya didn't fuss or cry, but simply stared wide-eyed into Rivka's weary dusk-blue eyes. She didn't know what Chaya could actually see, maybe shapes, maybe colors, but she could already tell her daughter was an observer, an old soul. Chaya seemed to experience the world through her eyes, as though she knew from the start that her gift of quiet observation would prove her saving grace.

As Rivka nursed Chaya, the radiator hummed with steamy warmth, lulling both of them into a deep, peaceful slumber. Outside, piles of freshly fallen snow dressed the bare tree branches in billowy white sleeves. For Antwerp, Belgium, it was a mild winter day.

When Rivka awoke, it was dark and her husband Zev was sitting next to her, beaming as he admired their firstborn child.

"Look at that," he said, as Chaya's tiny fingers wrapped around his calloused thumb. His hazel eyes crinkled with delight as he took in the sight of his daughter, resting in his strong, gentle arms.

Zev had brought the Yiddish newspaper with him, which was now sprawled on the floor.

"Any news?" asked Rivka.

"Pretty much the same as yesterday, worded a bit differently perhaps," said Zev. "Who knows what we're supposed to believe anymore."

Rivka knew what he meant. Most of the news was propaganda—swayed toward Hitler's Nazi party.

"I get better news from the barber," he said, kicking away the pile.

The nurse came in holding something in her hand, and glanced down at the scattered newspaper. Zev smiled apologetically and bent down to pick it up, while cradling Chaya with his other arm.

"I can get it," she said, and placed the newspaper in the bin. "This piece of paper you'll want to keep." The nurse smiled as she handed Chaya's birth certificate to Rivka.

"Can you hand me my purse?" Rivka asked Zev.

He reached down and got it for her. Rivka opened the purse and tugged at some loose stitches. They secured a hidden pocket she had sewed inside the lining.

Rivka knew better than to keep personal documents in view. After the Germans invaded Belgium, they took records of everyone who lived there. They now knew that Rivka and Zev were Jews—Hitler's primary target. But Chaya had just been born. According to the Germans, she did not exist, and Rivka intended to keep it that way. Rivka folded the birth certificate and tucked it into the bottom of the hidden pocket.

CHAPTER TWO

Taken Away

Rivka, August 1941

The clock read 2:00 a.m. The low thud of a rifle banged against the front door.

"Open up!" yelled a voice in German.

Zev and Rivka flew out of bed. Rivka saw the panic in Zev's eyes as he threw on his clothes and ran toward the entry.

"Stay here!" he whispered to her. "Don't make a sound!"

He closed the bedroom door behind Rivka and Chaya, who was sitting in her crib, eyes wide with alarm. Rivka scooped her up just as she began to wail.

"Open up!" yelled the man at the door.

A rifle shot sounded in the town square below.

Rivka opened the bedroom door a crack, just enough to see what was happening. Zev's hands shook as he unbolted the door. As soon as the lock unclicked, a burly, babyfaced soldier—no older than 17 or 18—swung open the door. He grabbed Zev by the arm, while another put a gun to Zev's back and yelled, "Go!" He turned around, pushing Zev out the apartment door.

Tears burned Rivka's eyes as she watched her husband be captured and taken away. As much as she wanted to act, there was nothing she could do without putting herself and her daughter in grave danger.

The door stood open like a mouth agape, channeling the sounds of anger, fear, and chaos. Rivka could hear more men being rounded up in the street. A woman screamed. A shot rang out. Then silence.

From the bedroom she could hear the sound of a metal door slamming, the rumbles of panic, and a final gunshot.

Rivka held tightly onto Chaya and leaned against the dresser to steady herself. A wave of nausea rose from the pit of her stomach. Her heart raced.

She'd heard rumors of Jews being taken away on cattle cars to labor camps, but had refused to believe them. Now she knew: the roundup of Jews was very real indeed.

As Rivka's body shivered with shock, images from that evening flashed through her mind like bolts of lightning. She closed her eyes and prayed for her husband's safety. She prayed for her family back home in Czechoslovakia. And she prayed for her little girl.

Her first instinct was to escape, but where to? Their friends and relatives were in just as much jeopardy as she was. Rivka paced, thinking about what to do, but she came up with nothing. *Maybe they won't come for us*, Rivka hoped.

She sat at the kitchen table motionless, staring out at nothing. As her eyes came into focus, she realized that Zev had left his wallet on the table. The gold-embossed initials were nearly worn off, the black leather now burnished from use. Rivka tucked the wallet into her robe pocket and held onto it as though holding onto him. Then she opened up her closet and pulled out her suitcase. *Better to be prepared*, she thought. *Just in case.*

Rivka searched through her drawers for whatever valuables she could find—opal earrings, a filigreed gold bracelet, Zev's pocket watch, a fur stole and muffler—and packed them into a suitcase, along with diapers and clothes for Chaya. She had only one photograph of her siblings and parents gathered together—at least most of them—along with her young niece and nephew. An image of her brother Meyer had been cut and pasted after the photo was taken, but it somehow managed to fit, if a bit awkwardly. Still, she treasured this image and didn't want to leave it behind.

Once she had finished packing, Rivka felt restless, like an animal pacing in a cage. As Chaya slept, she sifted through the newspaper, hoping to find some answers or even a clue. But she found nothing. Sure, there were articles about the war, but mostly about events far away, and even those were misleading and vague.

Without useful news, without knowing what to do, Rivka felt like time was standing still. The wall clock's tick-tock, once barely audible, now seemed to echo throughout the flat, as though sounding their final hours.

Rivka looked outside. It was an especially beautiful day, cloudless and bright. She normally loved the sunshine. Today it hurt her eyes.

CHAPTER THREE

The Fateful Knock

Rivka, October 1941

Rivka's nights were fitful—images of the night Zev was captured plagued her, making it hard to sleep. She talked to neighbors, to merchants and anyone else who seemed safe enough to question, to help her figure out what to do. Many of her neighbors had already left, though she didn't know if they had escaped or been taken away. All she could do was wait. And hope. And pray.

The fateful knock came in the middle of the night, two months after Zev's arrest. Rivka heard a loud pounding on the door. Seconds later, two soldiers burst through, having kicked the door open. Splinters of painted wood littered the entry. Chaya, woken by the commotion, began to cry. Rivka jumped out of bed and wrapped a robe over her worn flannel nightgown. She picked up her daughter and held her close.

One of the soldiers impatiently prodded Rivka with the tip of his rifle. Dark circles under his eyes and a shadow of stubble hinted at his lack of sleep.

"*Gehen!* We must go! Now!"

Rivka nearly lost her balance, but held Chaya tight. She looked back at the soldier. He looked right past her, as though he was simply clearing out debris.

No amount of planning could have prepared Rivka for the fear that engulfed her. The cobblestone street below echoed the shrieks and cries of women and children. Soon she would be among them.

Rivka's hands shook, but she managed to slip on her shoes, then bundled up Chaya and grabbed her suitcase. As she descended the stairs, her neighbor Vivette leaned close as if to say good-bye.

Instead, she whispered in rapid Flemish. "You must tell the officer you're Hungarian, and that your husband works for the Germans. Tell him this is all a mistake. Tell him you're not Jewish and you shouldn't be there. Listen to me. You must do this."

Rivka looked into Vivette's warm brown eyes and nodded. She squeezed her neighbor's hand as if to say, "Thank you," then lurched forward as the hard metal of a rifle jabbed her back.

"Get in line!" a soldier yelled. He pushed her into a truck packed with women and children, then bolted shut the heavy doors. Rivka covered Chaya's ears with her scarf to muffle the passengers' anguished cries. Through a small, rusted window, Rivka watched her home grow smaller and smaller as the truck ambled over the bumpy, potholed road.

Sleepy, frightened children clung to their mothers in the cramped, suffocating space. Each bump in the road sent children flying. Motion sickness got the better of some, while others soiled themselves from fright. The nauseating stench, mixed with the unbearable heat, made every moment seem like an eternity.

When the truck finally stopped and the door opened, a welcome burst of fresh air filled Rivka's lungs. Her relief subsided, however, as soon as her eyes adjusted to the dimly lit camp, surrounded by barbed wire. A sign read "*SS-Sammellager Mecheln*" in German, along with a bright red swastika, the symbol of the Nazi party. They had arrived in Malines.

Soldiers herded Rivka, Chaya, and the other women and children through the dry, dusty camp to one of the many cold cement bunkers that were little more than oversize toolsheds. There was no plumbing, no food, or even a drop of fresh water. While only a half hour from Antwerp, this place felt to Rivka like another world.

Hunger, thirst and fatigue overwhelmed her. She huddled alongside the other women and children and closed her eyes, trying to forget, trying to sleep, trying to dream she was back in the comfort of home—anywhere but there.

But Rivka couldn't sleep, so she sat quietly and nursed Chaya, even though she knew it provided little more than comfort for her hungry child. Nearby, a little girl resting on the hard, unforgiving ground started at Rivka with bright green eyes. The girl scooted up to Rivka, and, without a word, leaned against her and closed her eyes.

Rivka stroked the sleeping girl's hair. It was jet-black with a widow's peak, just like her youngest sister's. She leaned against the wall of the bunker and closed her eyes. Images flowed through her mind: Zev, her parents, her brothers and sisters. She wondered if she'd ever see them again.

CHAPTER FOUR

A Secret Gift

Rivka, October 1941

Just before dawn, a guard walked toward Rivka and Chaya, one hand stuck deep in his coat pocket. His other hand rested idly on a large black gun anchored to his belt. Rivka sat up straight and breathed deeply, trying to calm her pounding heart. The guard stopped in front of Rivka and looked around. As he pulled his hand out of his pocket, Rivka shuddered.

The guard glanced toward Chaya, who smiled up at him. Warmth flashed in the soldier's eyes, then quickly faded. With one swift motion, he took Rivka's hand and placed in it something smooth and round and perfectly white: a boiled egg.

"For your baby," he whispered.

Then he turned on his heels and walked back toward the officer's quarters.

Rivka held the egg in her hand. The shell looked almost bluish white in the sunlight. Slowly, she peeled away the shell. Then she took a tiny piece and gave it to Chaya, who opened her mouth like a hungry bird. "You can at least still nurse, but the others can't," said Rivka softly, gazing down at her hungry daughter.

Rivka looked around at all the other children, huddled with their mothers, eyeing the egg. Still holding Chaya, Rivka stood up, divided the egg into tiny pieces, and gave a taste of this secret gift to as many children as she could.

"Do you have any more?" one child asked. "I'm so hungry."

"I'm sorry. That's all I have," said Rivka sadly.

The other children looked up with the same hollow, hungry gaze. *If only they could have a sip of water, a piece of bread*, thought Rivka. With the exception of this unexpected gift, the soldiers ignored them, and there was nothing to forage—not even a sliver of fresh grass or a wild berry.

Three days passed without food or water, and Rivka's worries were mounting. Her milk supply was waning from dehydration, and Chaya was starting to get sick. Still, Chaya didn't cry out from hunger or thirst. She kept as quiet as everyone else at the camp—eerily quiet, as though she, like the other children there, understood the vital importance of staying silent.

Rivka looked at her listless child. The parting words of her neighbor echoed in her mind: *Tell them you're Hungarian, that your husband works for the Germans…* There had been no opportunity to say anything when she was herded into the truck. Now was the time.

CHAPTER FIVE

Changing of the Guards

Rivka, October 1941

Rivka thought about her kindly neighbor's advice. Vivette meant well, but would lying about her heritage actually work? Rivka knew how to speak German. With her honey-colored hair and blue eyes, she looked like she could be a non-Jew. But she was dressed just like all the other Jewish women forced out of their homes in the middle of the night. Looking down at her dusty nightclothes, Rivka doubted an officer would ever believe her. Still, she had to try. But first she had to get past the guard.

Rivka recognized a woman from her town, the baker's wife, Brigitte. Short and stocky, she had the ropy forearms of someone who kneaded bread for a living. Her usually round, ruddy cheeks now looked deflated, drained of color. Hunger and thirst had clearly taken a toll on her.

As Rivka approached, Brigitte looked up, and smiled weakly, "Rivka. So good to see you."

Rivka leaned over and gave her a warm hug. Tears welled up in Brigitte's cloudy gray eyes. "They took my family away. My husband. My sons."

"They took away Zev, too," said Riva sympathetically.

They sat together quietly until a loud gurgle from Chaya broke the silence. Both women smiled.

"Can I hold her?" asked Brigitte. "It's been so long since I held a baby. My boys are all grown up." A shadow ran across her face, but then she looked down at Chaya and her face softened again. "What a beauty, *keneinahora*! *Oi*—those dimples!" She gently squeezed Chaya's pudgy cheek.

"Would you mind watching her for a little while?" asked Rivka.

"I need to go speak to someone."

"Of course," said Brigitte. She paused, then asked hesitantly, "Who do you need to see?"

"I need to speak to one of the officers," Rivka answered.

Brigitte looked thoughtfully at Rivka. "Go. Do what you need to do," she said.

"Thank you," said Rivka. She gave Chaya a kiss, placed her on Brigitte's lap, and headed toward the officers' quarters.

Rivka watched and waited for the changing of the guards. There would be a brief moment—maybe a minute or two—when a guard wasn't present. She slipped by as soon as the first guard left his post and went to get his replacement. Then she walked to the officer's station.

Still wearing her robe and nightgown, Rivka approached the officer's secretary. In perfect German, without a trace of her Yiddish accent, she said, "I need to speak to the officer."

The secretary smirked at Rivka's shabby robe. "He's busy," she said dismissively.

"It's very important," said Rivka.

"Yes, I'm sure it is," said the secretary while scrawling something in her notebook.

"I'll wait," said Rivka, and sat down.

She had made it this far. She was determined to speak with the officer, no matter how long it took.

Another woman was waiting in the same room. Unlike Rivka, she was fully dressed in a tailored suit and expensive heels, now scuffed and caked with dirt. Her glossy black hair was in a disheveled bun and her eyes were bloodshot and swollen.

"I shouldn't be here," the other woman said to the secretary. "I'm not supposed to be here," she mumbled to herself. In her hand was an embroidered handkerchief, balled into her palm. The frayed blue edges peered out from her hand, streaked with tears and dirt.

After nearly two hours, the officer opened his door. The woman who arrived before Rivka was allowed in. Even though the office door was closed, the walls were thin. Rivka could easily overhear their conversation.

"I'm not supposed to be here!" she cried. "I'm not a Jew. My husband works for the Germans. I was brought here by mistake!"

"Why should I believe you?" the officer barked.

The woman paused. "Because it's true!" said the woman. "Give me my things and I'll show you! Let me show you my papers. Please!"

"Send her back," said the officer without another look at her, and shoved the woman out of the office.

"But I'm not one of them! I'm not supposed to be here!" she cried again, this time burying her face in her handkerchief.

Rivka watched as a guard led the woman, now hysterical, away. Sobbing, she stopped to blow her nose. The guard pushed her forward, causing her to trip and fall to the ground.

"Get up!" he yelled, but she sat there, crying.

Finally, he lifted her up and flung her over his shoulder like a sack of flour. Her sobs grew softer and softer until all Rivka could hear were the rhythmic steps of boots marching across the hardened ground.

There is absolutely no chance the officer will believe me, thought Rivka. *Not after this.* But there was no turning back. She and Chaya hadn't had food or water in three days, and Chaya was getting sick. Rivka took a deep breath. "May I speak with the officer now?" she asked the secretary.

"You'll have to wait," said the secretary, not bothering to lift her eyes from her reading.

Rivka sat back down. Maybe it wasn't such a bad thing waiting awhile longer, especially after what she just saw. From inside the officer's office came the sounds of liquid pouring into a glass. Probably beer or vodka even. Having grown up on a property that housed a tavern and Saturday night music hall, Rivka knew what men were like after a few drinks. She would wait until the officer had finished whatever he was drinking. But she would not wait for the secretary, who obviously had no intention of letting her in.

Rivka heard laughter from the officer's quarters. Now was the time. She stormed past the secretary, knocked loudly on the door, and barged in.

"Do you know your secretary has been making me wait here all this time?" Rivka said in perfect German. She didn't wait for him to respond. "My husband is an officer in the Hungarian army and works for the same people as you. I could get you fired for this!" she spat.

The officer, momentarily sobered, looked at Rivka. "Then what are you doing here? And why are you in your nightgown?"

Rivka was quick on her feet. "Your soldiers came and took me and my baby in the middle of the night. They refused to listen. We were not supposed to be here. And now my child is sick. You must let us go," demanded Rivka, eyes blazing.

"Where is your baby now?" asked the officer.

"One of the women over there is watching her for me," Rivka said. "I will get her as soon as I finish speaking with you. But you need to let us go."

The officer looked down as if to check his record book, then looked up at Rivka's beautiful face.

After what felt like an eternal silence, he said, "I'm very sorry about this mistake. Go get your daughter. We'll get your bags, and I'll have someone take you out of here."

Rivka stared in disbelief, forgetting to breathe. Then she exhaled in relief, almost losing her balance.

"How soon can we go?" she asked, not wanting to wait another second.

"I'll see when the next train leaves," said the officer.

Rivka walked past the secretary, who was now sitting upright, eyes wide. Only after Rivka passed the guards did she allow herself to digest what had just happened. *I can't believe it. Thank you God*, she thought. It was a miracle. She and Chaya would be freed from the camp.

Rivka returned to the barracks where Chaya was sleeping in Brigitte's lap. "Thank you, Brigitte, for watching Chaya. I'm sorry it took so long, but they made me wait," said Rivka, who reached down to hug Brigitte's shoulders, then gathered

Chaya into her arms.

A guard waited by the open entry of the barracks.

"Let's go."

Rivka gently touched Brigitte's shoulder, bidding her good-bye. Brigitte looked up, concerned. Being taken away by a guard didn't usually lead to good things.

Rivka followed the guard, who moved quickly across the camp. He clearly didn't like being around the prisoners, and wanted to get away as quickly as possible. Rivka held Chaya closely as she ran to keep up with him.

Near the entry Rivka spotted a cavernous room filled with rows and rows of luggage. "May I take my suitcase?" asked Rivka. She feared asking, but knew her most valuable possessions were packed inside.

"If you can find it," said the guard.

Her plain leather suitcase looked like so many others. The only thing that set it apart was a frayed red ribbon tied to the handle.

Rivka paced back and forth looking for her suitcase. After nearly giving up her search, she spotted the ribbon. "There it is," she said. The guard lifted it up from the pile and placed it on the back of a small, open truck.

The train station was only minutes away. The guard brought out the suitcase for Rivka, then handed her two train tickets and, without a word, drove away. Carrying Chaya with one arm and her suitcase and tickets with the other, Rivka boarded the train, anxious for it to leave before the officer changed his mind and came back for her.

As she waited for the train to depart, Rivka's heartbeat sounded louder to her than the station clock that towered overhead. She wouldn't believe she was truly out of Malines until the doors closed and the train was moving. When it finally pulled out of the station, Rivka exhaled deeply. She looked at Chaya, now sound asleep, blissfully unaware that they had just been escorted out of prison by their captors.

As the train headed toward Antwerp, trucks were just pulling in to Malines. They were there to pick up the inmates—thousands of women and children, young and old. Only they weren't going home. They were headed to Auschwitz.

CHAPTER SIX

Coming Home

Rivka, October 1941

As the train pulled into the Antwerp station, Rivka looked out the window. Uniformed guards paced across the platform, their swastika-banded arms hanging motionless by their sides as their eyes darted back and forth, searching for Jews.

A stillness hung in the air like a lingering fog. People milled around the street with hats pulled low, walking swiftly, staring at nothing but the road ahead. No one dared look directly at the armed guards for fear of being arrested for no other reason than appearing suspicious.

Holding Chaya tightly in one arm, Rivka dragged her heavy suitcase with the other and made her way back home. The town square, normally filled with bustling street vendors, was now eerily quiet.

Rivka's stomach lurched as she turned the corner and spotted a crudely hammered sign hanging limply in a crevice of an old stone wall. It read: *Todesstrafe für Juden zu verstecken*—Penalty of Death for Hiding Jews. Who would help her now?

Drenched in sweat, Rivka took a deep breath as she finally reached her front door. She was greeted by an ugly slash of yellow paint, with dried drips that streamed towards the ground like a frozen trail of tears. Other doors nearby shared the same angry mark, signaling that Jews had lived there. Still splintered from the break-in, the door was closed, but no longer bolted. Entering was easy. Staying there would not be.

Rivka longed to return to the familiar comfort of home, but the ever-present Nazi soldiers would notice any sign of movement or unfamiliar sound, especially Chaya's crying. If they were discovered, they would be taken right back to the camps. But where else could they go? Besides, there was still a bit of food left in the cupboards, and they were desperately hungry. There was simply no other choice.

Slowly, stealthily, Rivka entered her apartment. *Just for now*, she thought, *until I can get a bit of food, figure out where else to go.* Everything was just as she had left it, and yet it all seemed so foreign, as though she was observing a snapshot of a life that was no longer her own. The warmth of family, the smell of fresh food, the sounds of life had been snuffed out forever the night they were taken away.

As Rivka leaned down to move her suitcase, her eye caught a glint of green. There was something on the floor by the entry—a small, emerald-colored matchbook. Neither Rivka nor Zev smoked. Maybe one of the soldiers dropped it? Rivka picked it up and took a closer look. She opened it to look inside. All the matches were still in tact. Above them, was a handwritten address, carefully printed in small, neat letters: 19 Vierstraat.

The address sounded familiar, but she couldn't place it. *Who lives on Vierstraat?* Her mind drew a blank. Rivka took a look at the matchbook cover: Louis Armstrong Special Cigars. *Where would someone get a fancy matchbook like this?* Rivka gazed at the gold emblem, then stashed it in her pocket. She held the matchbook, rubbing her thumb against the imprint, thinking.

She looked through the cabinets and found an old box of matzoh left over from the previous Passover. The holiday was fast approaching, and she felt fortunate to have some of this "unleavened bread" to feed herself and Chaya. She was so hungry, having not eaten anything for days, that she could've eaten the whole box and the cardboard, too. But she knew better—she had to make it last. She gave Chaya a little piece to suck on.

Rivka turned on the faucet, wondering if there would still be running water. A drizzle of lukewarm liquid poured from the nozzle. It was wet and a little rusty, but certainly better than nothing. After taking a few glorious mouthfuls and splashing some water on her face, she filled a baby bottle and gave it to Chaya, who drank it eagerly.

Rivka sorted through the cupboard as quietly as she could, and found her rations, still in the same place she left them. There were some oats in a tin, as well as powdered milk and a little sugar. She added some water and cooked all three together. After going without food for days, the sweet warmth of this porridge was as satisfying as anything she'd ever tasted. Chaya ate heartily, grinning with a mouthful of porridge, which made Rivka smile for the first time in weeks.

While she knew her time there was fleeting, Rivka allowed herself to sit down long enough to savor a cup of hot tea while Chaya napped. She looked around the flat and said a prayer. At least for the moment, they were safe.

But what about Zev? Rivka had no idea where he was, how to find him, or if he was even alive. She took out Zev's passport photo from the wallet he'd left and gazed at it, wishing she could talk to him, find out if he was okay. *Please God, let us see him again,* she prayed.

CHAPTER SEVEN

Vivette

Rivka, November 1941

Chaya and Vivette

Rivka knew she was no longer safe at the place she'd called "home." But she had no idea where to go. Without somewhere to hide, she and Chaya would certainly be found and taken back to the camps. It was just a matter of time.

Before the war, Rivka knew she could always find support and shelter with her family in Czechoslovakia, her relatives in Antwerp, or her Jewish friends nearby. But as far as she knew, they had all been taken away to the camps, or, like her, were in hiding. Then she remembered Vivette, the neighbor who had whispered to her that fateful night.

Rivka recalled Vivette's parting words: "You must tell the officer you're Hungarian, and that your husband works for the Germans. Tell him this is all a mistake. Tell him you're not Jewish and you shouldn't be there." This advice had helped save Rivka's life, and she was eternally grateful. She decided to take Chaya to Vivette's to thank her, to let her know she had survived. Maybe she'll let us stay with her for awhile, Rivka hoped.

Vivette was a devout Catholic in her late sixties, widowed shortly before Chaya was born. She had a grown son who had since moved away to Switzerland, married, and started a family of his own. He rarely visited, and Vivette was often alone.

Rivka first met Vivette when she was pregnant with Chaya. She had heard about the passing of Vivette's husband and paid a visit to introduce herself. Vivette's face lit up when she first met Rivka, who waited at the front door holding a sponge cake atop her distended belly. "I see you have a tray for your cake!" said Vivette as she welcomed Rivka inside, and both women laughed. "Yes, I'm expecting in just a few weeks," said Rivka, still smiling as she placed the cake on Vivette's lace-covered table.

When Chaya was born, Vivette knit a beautiful hat and booties for her in white lambswool. When she turned six months old, Vivette brought over a baby blanket in the same soft, snowy wool. Knowing how much Vivette loved children, Rivka began taking Chaya to visit, often bringing with her a home-made cake or strudel for tea. Soon, this became a regular routine, one that never ceased to brighten Vivette's otherwise solitary days.

Rivka bundled up Chaya and put on a knit hat and scarf, hoping to be as inconspicuous as possible while walking outside. Luckily, Vivette's apart-ment was only just down the street. Rivka held Chaya close to her face, hoping no one would notice her. She felt her pulse quicken as she approached a soldier, his drab uniform punctuated by a fist-size swastika framed in red. He brushed past her, not giving her a second glance.

Rivka took a deep breath as she spotted Vivette's Dutch-blue door. She knocked gently three times. On previous visits, Vivette would often yell, "I'm coming!" as she shuffled toward the door, but this time Rivka met with silence. Her stomach dropped. Had Vivette been taken away, too?

Just as Rivka was about to turn away, she heard some movement from behind the door. She knocked again. The door slowly opened and Vivette peered out. When she saw it was Rivka, she gasped. Her jaw slackened, as though she had seen a ghost.

"Rivka?" she whispered. "I can't believe you're here...that you're back."

"I can hardly believe it myself," said Rivka.

Vivette gazed at Chaya, who was still half asleep, her soft, flushed cheek resting on Rivka's shoulder. Vivette gently placed her small, cupped hand on Chaya's cheek and smiled at her warmly, then looked up at Rivka and out toward the street. "What am I thinking letting you stand out there?

Please, come in. Come in!" she said as she whisked Rivka inside.

While Vivette prepared coffee, she told Rivka what life had been like since she'd left. "It's just not the same," she said. "There's no life. Everyone hides in their house with their shutters closed. So many people are gone, even more after you left..." she trailed off, thinking to herself. "Has anyone else come back?" asked Rivka hopefully. Vivette sighed, then said, "If they have, I wouldn't know."

Vivette set down some dry biscuits and sat down. "It's not much, but at least I have rations. I miss your delicious apple strudel," she smiled, revealing a gold-capped tooth. Rivka thought about all the ingredients she would need to make an apple strudel—flour, butter, apples, sugar—and recalled the long wooden table her mother used to spread out the dough "as thin as paper" before rolling it up. Yes, she, too, missed these simple luxuries, though they were hardly on the forefront of her mind. What she needed was shelter, somewhere safe to hide.

"I would be happy to cook for you if you would let us stay for awhile, just until we find another place," said Rivka, seizing the moment. "I could also do your cleaning and sewing," she added.

Vivette lifted her eyebrows in surprise.

"You want to stay here?" she said. Her posture turned cold and distant, an abrupt change from the warm, welcoming presence she'd known before the war. Sensing Vivette's resistance, Rivka felt her stomach clench.

"If I could go home, I would, but I can't live there anymore," said Rivka. "They know that we—that Jews—lived there. There's a sign on the door..." Rivka trailed off, clearly worried. *Please, Vivette. We have nowhere else to go.*

Vivette sat quietly, thinking to herself. Her gaze landed on Chaya, who smiled at her, then reached out her tiny hand. Vivette responded instinctively, and leaned forward to hold her. With Chaya in her arms, Vivette's warmth returned.

"How can I say no to a little beauty like you," said Vivette to Chaya. She turned to Rivka, "Yes, of course you can stay here. Stay as long as you need to."

"Oh, thank you Vivette!" said Rivka. "Thank you." Despite her relief, Rivka remained uneasy about Vivette's initial coldness, hesitation. She took a deep breath and sighed, hoping the feeling in the pit of her stomach was just a case of nerves.

CHAPTER EIGHT

Friend or Foe?

Rivka, November 1941

Vivette's apartment smelled like an old lady—musty and over-perfumed—and its drawn shades made the place seem even more somber than it had been prior to the war. Vivette had an extra room that had been her son's, but had been changed into a small sitting room when he moved away.

"All I have for you to sleep on is this," she said, pointing to a chaise she kept covered with an old crocheted shawl.

"Anything is fine," said Rivka, trying to be accommodating.

Vivette brought over two thin wool blankets and a flattened feather pillow.

"It's not much, but you're welcome to use them."

Rivka knew Vivette had plenty of fine linens in her hall closet, but she did not dare question her. "Thank you," said Rivka graciously.

As Rivka and Chaya got situated, Vivette went down the hall for a nap. Chaya stared at a trail of dust that floated along a small stream of sunlight. While Vivette slept, Rivka straightened up the apartment, dusting and sweeping while balancing Chaya on her hip. Staying busy was the best way to stop her mind from racing. *Don't think too much*, she told herself. *Vivette is doing a kindness by having us stay. I should feel grateful.* But something nagged at her.

For the first few days, Vivette treated Rivka and Chaya as welcomed guests, appearing to savor their company.

"It's good to have a baby in the house again!" she said, and thanked Rivka often for her help.

But as the days turned into weeks, Vivette's gentle requests turned into impatient demands. Rivka was soon tending to Vivette as maid, cook, and seamstress.

"If you're going to stay here, you'll need to pay your way," mumbled Vivette one morning while eating a mouthful of toast.

Rivka turned to Vivette, but was at a loss for words.

"Room and board aren't free, you know! The least you can do is pay me something, a little something. What about that crystal bowl you had on your dining table, you know the one?"

Rivka knew exactly which one. Vivette had commented on it the first time she had visited. It had been a wedding present from Rivka's aunt, hand-cut from Prague.

"Yes," said Rivka, quietly. "I'll get it for you today."

Rivka went as quickly as she could to her flat, wrapped the bowl in a towel, and brought it back to Vivette's. After giving Vivette this valuable piece, Rivka assumed she would be satisfied. But the bowl was just the beginning.

Soon Vivette was demanding Rivka's silver, jewelry, and china.

"Do you know what the price of hiding a Jew is, Rivka? My life! Those earrings are nothing compared to my sacrifice," said Vivette the following week, recalling a pair of pearl earrings Rivka had worn.

Rivka knew she had no choice. Slowly, stealthily, she went back to retrieve more valuables.

But there was one thing Rivka was not willing to give away— a Persian lamb coat Zev had tailored especially for her. When Vivette expressed interest in it, Rivka politely declined.

"I'm sorry, Vivette, but Zev made this for me. It was an engagement present."

It comforted her to wear it. Plus, it was the warmest coat she owned. Vivette looked up, silent at first. Then she slapped Rivka across the face.

Shocked, Rivka didn't feel the sting at first, but then it came. A hot, hand-shaped welt rose on Rivka's cheek. Sensing her mother's pain, Chaya began to cry.

"Who do you think you are?" seethed Vivette. "You're nothing! Don't you think I could open my doors to those soldiers any day of the week? Now give me that coat!"

Rivka stood there in shock. Her heart raced, knowing that Vivette had turned. Gone was the sweet, grandmotherly widow who had doted on Chaya and cherished Rivka's visits. In her place was a lonely woman drunk with greed and power, Rivka knew she couldn't stay there a moment longer. Holding Chaya tight, she dashed to her room, grabbed her belongings, and fled.

She returned to her house and quickly gathered whatever food she could carry in her purse—a small sack of oats, a tin of powdered milk, a few pieces of matzoh—and her suitcase. From the look of the brewing clouds, she could tell that the light mist would soon turn to thunderstorms.

Bundled in her fur coat, Rivka blended into the crowds milling along the city streets. She reached into her pocket for a handkerchief and felt something beneath it. The matchbox. She picked it up and looked at the handwritten address, 19 Vierstraat.

Who lives on Vierstraat? Rivka thought about everyone she knew—her friends, her relatives, merchants, neighbors—but no one came to mind. She stared at the emerald cover again, embossed with the words, "Louis Armstrong Special Cigars" in swooping gold letters. Then Rivka remembered. The address was not someone's home, but a warehouse, owned by a furniture mover named Louis.

CHAPTER NINE

On The Train

Rivka, January 1942

The snow fell so swiftly it formed a powdery blanket atop the pot-holed brick roads, making walking across town especially challenging, especially as the clouds blotted out the afternoon light. The train station was just a few blocks away, so Rivka headed in that direction, holding Chaya tight.

Rivka found a seat towards the back of the train car, sat down and took off her scarf. Gently shaking it out, she accidentally dripped the melting snow on Chaya. She looked up with her rosy cheeks and smiled, licking at the drops.

"Ah, you're thirsty," said Rivka. "I'll give you some milk just as soon as we get there."

Rivka gathered bits of icy snow that had settled on her wool hat and fed them to Chaya. She smiled, as though it was a game.

Moments before departing, a German guard stepped onto the train. He clicked his heels, stared straight ahead, and ordered, "Attention passengers: I will need to check your bags. Please take out your passports."

Rivka felt the color drain away from her face. Paralyzed by fear, she stayed completely still and awaited her fate. Yes, she had her passport, and it revealed nothing. But the evidence was there—the matzoh hidden inside her purse would tell the guard everything he needed to know: she was a Jew.

The guard checked each person's bag, one by one. The seconds grew into minutes, accelerating her heart beat as the guard neared. Soon it would be her turn. *What would they do with her? With Chaya?* Rivka closed her eyes and prayed. *Please don't look in my purse.*

When she opened her eyes, the soldier had passed. He had passed her by! Perhaps he thought she was sleeping, or that he didn't want to disturb her because she was holding a baby. Either way, her prayer was answered. Another miracle had just occurred.

Rivka breathed a deep sigh of relief and then kept her eyes closed until the guard left the train. He did not try to rouse her, nor reach for her bag. Two people were escorted off the train, an elderly woman and a teenage boy. Rivka felt for them. *That could have been us.*

When her stop arrived, she quickly got up and off the train. She wrapped her shawl around Chaya as she neared the exit. Knowing that now, for a second time, she and her daughter had narrowly escaped, the heavy rains and gloomy clouds seemed to Rivka as welcoming as the sunniest summer day.

CHAPTER TEN

The Warehouse

Rivka, January 1942

The freshly fallen snow made the ground sparkle, shimmering like diamonds in the twilight. While the snowstorm had abated, it was still freezing, and Chaya was shivering. Rivka was thankful to see Vierstraat just ahead.

The address was barely noticeable, a modest display of numbers carved in stone. A gilded sign on the door read, "Moens Furniture Movers" in Flemish, now weathered with age. It had been several years since Zev worked with Louis Moens, but their friendship had endured.

Rivka turned the knob. The door was locked. "How am I supposed to get in?" she thought, beginning to panic. *Is this a trap? Am I too late?* Rivka looked around—at the door, the ground, the wall—then she saw it: a tiny, wilted envelope emerging from a crack in the stone. In it Rivka found a single key. She dried her hand and slid the worn brass key in the door.

To her great relief, the door unlocked. Inside, the place was dark, damp and dusty. As far as Rivka could tell, there was no electricity, no running water or source of heat. But they were safe, at least for now.

A ray of light poured in through the leaded glass window above the door, leading Rivka's eyes towards a workbench piled with long-abandoned scraps of upholstery fabric. On the bench was a piece of paper, looking just as worn and dusty as the rest of the items there. But it had her name on it, written in the angular, careful penmanship of an architect.

Rivka turned the paper over and there it was—a letter from Louis.

Dear Rivka,

I passed by your house the other day, but no one was there.

I don't know where you and Zev are, but I thought I'd take a chance,

in case you made it back home. I only wish I could have done something sooner.

This place isn't much, but you can stay here for as long as you wish.

There is some fabric you can use for blankets in the back,

and some pads that can serve as beds. Use whatever you like.

I ran into Zev a few months ago, and told him that no matter

what happens, I'll do my best to stay in contact. Let me know

where you are from time to time—same spot as the key.

Stay safe, Louis

Rivka folded the letter and put it in her pocket. Zev had mentioned that he'd run into Louis, but had not said anything about him keeping track of the family. Perhaps he didn't want to worry her. At least now she knew that there was someone out there who could look out for her. "First thing we need to do is dry off," said Rivka to Chaya. She rubbed her hands together, then played peek-a-boo with a scrap of old velvet, making Chaya smile, her little teeth still chattering.

Rivka looked around the factory, scouring for fabric she could use to make a bed for Chaya. Most of it was cold and stiff and smelled of mildew. Rivka covered a piece of foam with layers of cotton and a musty woolen swath, and put Chaya to bed. She wrinkled her nose from the dust, coughed a few times, then settled in and went to sleep.

The next morning, Rivka emptied one of her suitcases, bundled up Chaya, and headed toward her house. She knew her time was limited, but she also knew that without ample warmth, neither she nor her daughter would survive the bone-chilling winter in Antwerp. She walked into the house, and pushed a chair against the broken door. Quickly, she packed as much bedding as she could into her suitcase, and some fresh clothes for Chaya, then just as quickly left the house.

Rivka learned where she could get food through the black market, but it didn't come cheap. "You want bread?" sneered a man who seemed to appear out of nowhere. He was short and bulbous with a waxed mustache and a prominent mole on the side of his weather-chapped nose. An ill-fitting felt hat cast a shadow over his deep-set eyes. Clearly, it had been a trade.

"The last person I sold to gave me her wedding band. Fresh food don't come cheap you know," he said.

Rivka opened her palm. All she had to offer were a handful of francs.

"You expect a loaf for those coins!" said the man, and laughed in her face. "You'll have to do better than that," and turned his attention away from her, curling his mustache as he scanned the area for customers.

Rivka stood back and watched an exchange. Had she not known this man was bartering, she would simply think he was greeting a friend. He would face huge fines, a prison sentence, or worse if he was caught, so subtlety was key.

A pocket watch was the price for a few cigarettes, a pair of hand-cobbled boots for a few strips of dried meat. "I have this fur," said Rivka, opening her purse, and passed the muffler to the man who looked at it critically.

"That's more like it," he smirked, and walked away.

Rivka followed him. The man moved surprisingly swiftly through the crowd, like a sure-footed dancer. He looked back at Rivka and signaled with a slight motion of his head and eyebrows, "Follow me."

Inside a small hut in the back of a store was what initially looked like an empty room with wooden crates. The man took the back of a hammer lying on one of the shelves, opened up the crate, and stealthily lifted a round loaf of bread from the box. He closed the wooden crate just as swiftly as he opened it, and wrapped the bread in newspaper. Rivka stuffed it in a fabric sack and headed back towards Louis' warehouse.

"I also need milk for my baby," said Rivka, trailing the man through the streets.

"Milk? Meet me tomorrow morning—4 a.m. I'll have some for you, but it'll cost you. I'll take the earrings you're wearing," he said.

Rivka lifted her fingers to her earlobe, having forgotten that she was wearing earrings. Her heart sank. They were simple but brilliant opals, the first gift Zev gave her when they moved to Belgium. She sighed, resigned.

"Okay. See you then," she said, and headed back with Chaya to the warehouse. There was no such thing as "fair trade" on the black market.

CHAPTER ELEVEN

The Longest Winter

Rivka, February 1942

When her valuables ran out, Rivka snuck back into her flat to retrieve whatever else she could find that might fetch her some food on the black market. She found very little that was of actual monetary value—the Nazis had already gone through drawers and cabinets, clearing out the last of her crystal and silver, all wedding presents from her family back in Czechoslovakia. Even their clothes and linens had been pilfered. What was once a home filled with warmth and life was now little more than a dusty, vacant shell.

Rivka searched the cabinets for any leftover rations that might still be of use. Short of a spoonful of dried milk and some moth-infested flour, there was nothing left. Before closing the door, Rivka looked back one last time, placed her hand on the doorframe's *mezuzah,* and headed back to the warehouse.

For the next eight months, the warehouse was Rivka's and Chaya's home. With only a few high, narrow windows, it welcomed little sunlight. The thick, stone walls preserved the winter chill long after the first spring buds appeared. On sunny days, Rivka took Chaya for walks.

"Let's go see the sunshine," Rivka would say to Chaya, and she'd beam with excitement.

They'd close their eyes and smile as the sun's warm rays soothed their muscles and instantly brightened their spirits. Rivka was careful though—going outdoors was risky—the Gestapo was everywhere. Walks were quick and brief—but they were as nourishing as the meager food that sustained them.

To pass the time, Rivka would tell Chaya stories while they rested on a makeshift bed made from old foam pads and a mishmash of mildewed upholstery. "Let's tell some stories," Rivka would say, recalling an earlier time when food was plentiful and her family was free. Even if Chaya didn't understand everything, it was something to do, and it helped Rivka keep her mind occupied, especially with fond memories of better times.

Rivka told Chaya about growing up among fruit orchards and farm animals near the base of the Carpathian mountains. "We grew and made everything ourselves. We even had a dance hall. Every Saturday people would come from all around the village to dance. Your Uncle Meyer—now he's someone who could really dance!" Rivka chuckled, just thinking about her raven-haired brother. He could make a broom handle look graceful.

Rivka remembered her father bringing "fresh milk—right from the cow" to each of his ten children in the morning, and biting into apples while they were still dangling on the tree. These recollections brought much-needed cheer to otherwise weary days.

Since the warehouse was full of fabric and thread, Rivka made some rag dolls for Chaya. Her favorite one had a soft velvet head. Chaya held it against her cheek and slept aside it, the fabric shedding violet fuzz on her sweaty face when she awoke. Chaya named it "Bébé." It was the second word she spoke after "Mama."

As their food supply dwindled, neither Rivka nor Chaya had the energy to do very much. Many days they would simply cuddle, trying to stay warm.

One morning, Chaya woke up with a fever. As the day progressed, her whole body seemed to be burning up without any sign of improvement. Living in a damp, cold warehouse with little nourishment had finally taken its toll. Rivka knew, however, that couldn't take Chaya to see a doctor. They couldn't risk being seen, or worse, identified as Jews. Rivka held her sickly child, feeling completely helpless. She knew they wouldn't survive if they stayed in the warehouse much longer.

Rivka learned where the rainwater collected along the sagging roof, and scooped up as much as she could to cool Chaya's burning skin and parched mouth. When her temperature finally broke, she remained very weak. Rivka decided it was time to contact Louis, even if it meant putting herself in danger.

On the tiny envelope that had once held the key, Rivka wrote: "Urgent: Baby's sick. Please help," and stuck it in the secret slot in between the two loose stones. Louis had already saved them once. She knew that his life would be in danger if the Gestapo ever learned he was helping them. But without food or medicine, Chaya wouldn't last another winter in the warehouse. It was time.

CHAPTER TWELVE

A Matchbook
From Saint Francis

Rivka, October 1942

Jilberte Delfosse

Rivka checked the secret slot each morning and evening, just before dawn and after dark. But each day, the note remained, growing more and more ragged as rain and wind battered the old stone wall.

One morning, after nearly three weeks, Rivka took a quick glance at the slot, expecting to find her tattered note still there. Instead, she found another matchbox. On the shiny garnet cover was a gold cross embossed with the name *Hospitaal Sint Francis*. Inside was an address and the name, Sister Rose.

Rivka didn't waste a moment. She picked up Chaya and walked towards Sint Francis, a small women's hospital on the outskirts of Antwerp. Its striking spires, mirroring its sister church, made it visible from afar. Rivka had walked past the old stone building, but had never been inside.

With hesitation, she and Chaya walked into the warm, sterile entry.

"I'm looking for Sister Rose," said Rivka to the nun working behind the front desk, and passed the matchbook to the nun.

"Aaaah," said the nun, nodding her head in understanding as she opened the familiar matchbook. A bowl full of them lay piled near the prayer candles. She looked up at Chaya, who smiled at her. "Follow me," she said.

Rivka and Chaya followed the compact, quick-footed nun as they ascended one staircase after another. When they arrived on the top floor, the nun took led them to a small corner room.

"Wait here please," she said, and just as briskly, closed the door and left. The patter of her heavy black shoes echoed as the nun returned to her post.

The room was no larger than a broom closet, but it was light and sunny—a welcome change from the dark, damp warehouse. Filled from floor to ceiling were piles of starched, white blankets. Sun shone through the divided glass window, warming the freshly laundered bedding. Both Rivka and Chaya snuggled against them.

"Mmm...doesn't that feel nice?" said Rivka to Chaya, who put her cheek against them. A random string dangled from the pile, and Chaya pulled on it. "No, mamela," gently taking her hand away. "You'll pull the whole pile down on you," and pointed to the tall, tightly folded stacks.

A quick, loud knock startled them. In walked an elderly nun, who seemed to carry with her a well of calm. Her presence was instantly soothing. A shock of thick, white hair peeked beneath her habit, illuminating her cornflower-blue eyes.

"My name is Sister Rose," said the nun in Flemish. "Louis is a cousin of mine. He told me about you and your child," and gently held Chaya's tiny hand.

"How old is she?" asked Sister Rose.

"She'll turn two in January," said Rivka.

"We know a family who is willing to take in a child," said Sister Rose. "They were planning to house a little boy, the son of a tailor, but the father changed his mind last minute. 'Nazis always need tailors to sew uniforms,' he told us. He thought they'd be safe. But no one is safe. The last I heard they were taken away, all three of them."

A shadow crossed Sister Rose's face. She sighed and whispered, "God bless them." She looked down and brushed her habit as if to swat off crumbs, took a deep breath, then looked up at Chaya and smiled.

"So, the good news is that this family can hide your daughter. They live in Wansin, a small town in Liege. Their daughter Jilberte is in training here to become a midwife."

Rivka knew better than to ask if she, too, could be hidden. Towns in Belgium were small and close-knit, even if the farms were spread far apart.

Neighbors knew each other and would talk if there was an adult stranger in town. A baby, however, could go largely unnoticed.

Rivka's throat constricted as she fought back tears. The thought of leaving Chaya was heartbreaking. But losing her to sickness or starvation would be far, far worse. Rivka gathered herself, but her voice came out as little more than a hoarse whisper.

"How soon?" she asked.

"You can go this afternoon," said Sister Rose. "Jilberte will be done with her shift in a few hours."

While they waited, Sister Rose brought in warm food and drinks for them—fresh bread and cheese and tea. It felt like a feast, but Rivka didn't have much appetite. Chaya chomped on her bread with vigor. She took a piece in her little hand and tried to feed Rivka, narrowly missing her mouth. "Oh, thank you, *mamela*," said Rivka, wiping the soggy crumbs from her cheek.

Rivka stared at her daughter and tried to take a mental snapshot of her face—her golden hair and bright hazel eyes, her rosy lips and dimpled cheeks.

"*Mein shaneh maideleh*," she said, and gave her kisses all over her face, which made Chaya giggle. *How do I explain that I need to leave her? That it's the only way to keep her safe?* Rivka kissed Chaya softly on the forehead and hugged her. She knew she would have to say good-bye, no matter how much her maternal instincts fought her.

In the warm room with her belly full, Chaya had one last nap cradled in Rivka's soothing arms. Just as the sun was setting, she was awoken by a soft knock on the door. A young girl, no older than 17 appeared. She was dressed in a traditional nurse's outfit, and her shiny auburn hair was pinned into a tidy bun.

"My name is Jilberte," she said in French. "I will take you home."

CHAPTER THIRTEEN

Good-Bye My Child

Rivka, October 1942

Rivka and Chaya

Rivka, Chaya, and Jilberte boarded the train. Rivka stared out the window, watching the blur of the city change to scattered buildings, then houses, then farmland. Chaya looked curiously at Jilberte, who made her laugh with a spontaneous game of peek-a-boo.

"I see you!" sang Jilberte from behind her outstretched fingers. Rivka watched Jilberte and Chaya play, and forced a smile.

"We're almost home," said Jilberte. "We get off at the next stop."

Jilberte's home was about a mile from the train station. Chaya stopped to say "hello" to a wandering dog, pick some wildflowers, and watch Belgian draft horses munch on a pile of fresh hay. By the time they arrived, Jilberte's parents were waiting. Their names were Gabrielle and Gaston, and they smiled broadly, clasping their hands with contained excitement as they saw Jilberte walking with Rivka and Chaya.

"This is Rivka and her daughter Chaya," introduced Jilberte in French. "Chaya will be two in January."

Rivka was fairly fluent, having traveled to the French-speaking side of Belgium before, but Chaya understood only Flemish mixed with the Yiddish her mother spoke. Rivka extended her arm to shake hands with Gabrielle. "Thank you," she said. "I can't thank you enough." She leaned her hand against the doorway, trying to stay upright as her knees began to buckle.

Gabrielle was a petite, compact woman with wavy brown hair and softly rounded features. She smoothed out her woolen dress and knelt down to greet Chaya, "Hello, Chaya! My name is Gabrielle. We're happy to meet you."

Chaya clung to her mother's leg. "I'm sorry. She doesn't speak French," said Rivka.

"I see," said Gabrielle, her brow furrowing.

"Would you like to stay for awhile and have some tea? Something to eat?" asked Gaston warmly.

"No, thank you," said Rivka. "I think the sooner I leave, the better," she said. "Chaya's never been away from me, even for a day." She stroked Chaya's silky hair. Chaya looked up and smiled. Rivka looked down at Chaya's open, loving face, and her eyes welled up with tears. She knew that if she stayed another minute, gave Chaya a hug or kiss good-bye, she could not bear to leave her.

Rivka grabbed her purse and headed toward the door. "I'll come visit as soon as I can," she said to the Delfosses. She looked one last time at Chaya, then turned her back and headed out as quickly as her feet would take her.

* * *

Chaya was momentarily distracted with the Delfosse's herding dog, Dowley, who licked her milky skin. When Chaya stood up to find her mother, Rivka was already gone. "Where's Mama?" she asked in Flemish.

"She went away for a little bit," said Gabrielle in French, understanding her gestures.

She extended her hand toward Chaya. "Let's go inside."

Having known only her mother's company, Chaya wanted nothing to do with this stranger.

"Mama?" she called again, her voice cracking.

"She is not here," said Gabrielle in French, but Chaya didn't understand.

Eyes wide with fear, she looked around. "Mama?" she whispered weakly. She ran toward the gate, shouting, "Mama! Come back!" She stood there, looking out, watching the distant figure of her mother grow smaller and smaller.

* * *

Rivka didn't dare turn around. She could hear her child wailing, calling her name. Not answering Chaya's pleas made her insides roil. Rivka crossed her arms tightly around her aching stomach and dug her nails into her palms. It was all she could do to keep herself upright. It took all her power not to turn around and rush back to her daughter, the person who needed her most in the world. Rivka headed towards the train station, eyes blurred from tears, blindly following the dirt road. Only after boarding the train did she finally collapse.

* * *

"Please, Mama, come back!"

Tears ran down Chaya's face, and she tried to run after her mother, but the front gate was locked. She put her tiny leg through the gate, and tried to squeeze through, but couldn't.

"Please come back, Mama!" she wailed. "Mama! Please!"

Gabrielle walked up to Chaya and knelt beside her. Tears ran down Gabrielle's cheeks as she gazed at Chaya. Hoarse and blotchy from screaming her mother's name, Chaya was exhausted from crying. Just barely two, she had been abandoned by the only constant in her life, the one person she had completely trusted.

"Let's go in," said Gabrielle, extending an open hand to lead her inside.

In shock, Chaya remained unmoving, her pudgy fingers still clinging to the front gate. She stared blankly at the winding road, looking for her mother to return, coming back to her as she always had.

"Mama," Chaya repeated, now almost a whisper, "Mama, don't go..."

Too exhausted to move, Gaston gently unhinged her fingers, and carried her inside.

A fireplace lent a warm glow to the living area. Chaya stared at the dancing flames, holding tightly onto her rag doll, Bébé, for comfort. She did not understand what these strange people were saying, nor what she was doing there. Lulled by the soothing fire and drained of all energy, Chaya fell into a deep sleep. She curled into a ball, clutching onto her doll, and dreamed of her mother.

CHAPTER FOURTEEN

A New Home

Chaya, October 1942

The Delfosse's house

When Chaya awoke the next morning, she looked around at the unfamiliar surroundings and panicked.

"Mama!" she called out. Then she remembered. Her mother was not there. Chaya thought of her mother's figure growing smaller and small. *Mama's gone.* A hollow feeling made her stomach ache. She clutched her belly, trying not to be sick.

"Good morning, Chaya!" said Gabrielle brightly. "Would you like some breakfast?"

Chaya looked at her, knowing that she was saying something nice, but could not understand.

Gabrielle tried again, "Are you hungry?" She mimed eating with a spoon. Chaya shook her head.

"I'll bring you a little something," said Gabrielle. "You can just taste it if you like, okay?"

Gabrielle went into the kitchen and brought Chaya a bowl of oatmeal with brown sugar and milk. The sweet, delicious smell made her forget all about feeling sick. She was suddenly very hungry.

"Thank you," she said in Flemish as she spooned heapfuls into her mouth, quickly emptying the bowl.

"Would you like some more?" asked Gabrielle, smiling. Chaya looked up at her blankly. Gabrielle showed Chaya the pot of porridge and lifted up a spoonful.

"More?"

"No, thank you," said Chaya.

Having had so little food for so long, her tiny stomach could not handle much. She had already eaten too fast and was feeling queasy.

Gaston kissed Gabrielle and rubbed Chaya gently on the head.

"Good morning!" he beamed in Flemish.

Gaston knew only a handful of words in Flemish, but they were comforting to Chaya, who was happy to hear these familiar sounds. His bouncy stride and lanky frame made him look even taller to Chaya, who gazed up at him curiously. When he smiled, his whole face seemed to light up—his cheeks creased like a rippling wave, and playful crinkles lit up his gray-blue eyes. Chaya instantly adored him.

"Would you like to go on a walk?" said Gaston to Chaya in broken Flemish. He mimed a silly walk, pointed outside, then extended his hand toward hers.

Chaya hesitantly took his hand and they walked around the Delfosse's small, neatly tended farm. Gaston pointed out the barn and said the word in French, and did the same when he pointed out the tractor, the sheep, the chickens and the cow. "Come, Dowley!" called Gaston, and his loyal black-and-white mutt came bounding enthusiastically toward him.

"Watch this!" Gaston said excitedly to Chaya, signaling her toward the sheep. Gaston opened up the gate to let Dowley inside the sheep's pen, then gave a long, loud whistle. Dowley understood the command. He ran circles around the small herd of sheep, gathering them into a tight bunch. Gaston whistled twice, and Dowley led them toward the barn. Gaston quickly opened the gate, let out three high-pitched whistles, and Dowley knew what to do—it was time for them to go inside. A storm was brewing.

Chaya beamed and clapped her hands. Gaston smiled, called Dowley to him and gently scratched his head.

"Good boy," he said.

"Good boy," Chaya repeated, and gently pet his silky ears. In return,

Dowley gave Chaya a big lick across her face. She wiped her mouth and giggled.

With a storm approaching, Gaston couldn't spend much more time outside with Chaya, but he knew just where to take her.

"Come," he said softly, and pointed to the top of the barn, where bales of hay were stored. Slowly, Gaston helped Chaya walk up the wooden ladder that led to the loft.

As they approached the top, they could hear soft-pitched mewing sounds and the rustling of hay. A litter of kittens, just weeks old, lay around their mother. There were six of them, two Calico, two tabby, one jet black and one soft gray. The ones who had finished nursing lay huddled in a heap, sleeping cozily. Chaya stared at this wondrous sight. She had never seen kittens before.

Gaston watched Chaya as she gazed at the sleeping kittens. She stretched out her little fingers and stroked the mama cat gently on its side. The mama cat purred.

"She's soft," said Chaya.

Sounds of thunder struck, startling the half-asleep kittens, who scooted closer to their mother, unfazed by the noise.

"Time to go back to the house," said Gaston, and carried Chaya down the ladder.

* * *

From the kitchen window, Gabrielle could see Gaston walking hand-in-hand across the yard, with Chaya, already a much different child than she'd seen the day before.

Still, the language barrier frustrated her. For many nights, Gabrielle cried as she went to sleep, frustrated that she was unable to communicate with the little girl she had taken into her home. But Chaya had a keen ear for language, and within a few weeks, could already understand most of what her "new family" was saying.

"She's like a sponge!" Gaston announced with enthusiasm after asking Chaya in French if she would like some cake for dessert.

Chaya nodded, "Yes, I would like some please" in perfect French.

* * *

After little more than a month, Chaya understood just about everything. Flemish words faded from memory as French became Chaya's primary language, and the Delfosse family became her own.

CHAPTER FIFTEEN

Maman & Papa Delfosse

Chaya, May 1943

Gabrielle and Dowley

Even though there was a war going on, life was as pleasant as it could be in the Belgian countryside. Chaya quickly adapted to life at the Delfosse's, and often walked around the farm on her own, bringing fresh grass for the sheep, tagging along with Dowley, and visiting the kittens, who were growing fast.

A neighbor at the next farm over had a daughter named Madeleine who was just a few months older than Chaya. Together, they played outside, chasing butterflies, searching for treasures, and watching the farm animals. They especially loved to roll down the hill. To adults, Madeleine's yard was barely more than a grassy slope. To Chaya, it felt like a mountain.

As carefree as they seemed, both Chaya and Madeleine were not strangers to the sounds of war. They knew how to find shelter and huddle into a ball if they ever heard the telltale sounds overhead. Streaming whistles from rockets led them instinctively to find safety, but did not prevent them from playing outside again the next day. Such was life during wartime, and that was all they knew.

Jilberte was often away at the hospital, working round-the-clock. Becoming a midwife took years of training, and at only seventeen years of age, she had just begun. Still, Jilberte treated Chaya like a little sister and would take time when she got home to sit and read to her or play with Bébé and Jilberte's own childhood doll, Elisabet, whose porcelain face and blinking eyes fascinated Chaya.

Every now and then, Jilberte would bring Chaya a special treat from the bakery on the way home from the hospital. Chocolate éclairs, Jilberte discovered, were her absolute favorite.

"Mmmm!" Chaya mumbled, her smiling mouth full of custard.

"I guess you like it!" laughed Jilberte, as she wiped chocolate off Chaya's nose and cheeks.

Gaston worked for the local newspaper and, like many people in the countryside, rode a bicycle to work. Sometimes he would ride Chaya on his bike and take her to work, letting her draw on blank newsprint, or just take her for a quick ride around town. On other days, Gaston would bring Chaya along as he herded the sheep with Dowley. When Chaya lagged behind, Dowley would circle back and nudge Chaya forward with his nose.

"Look," Gaston would cry. "He's herding you, too!"

Gabrielle, while less demonstrative than Gaston, was just as loving. She came to care for Chaya as she would her own child, and Chaya soon regarded Gabrielle as her second mother. While braiding her hair one morning, Chaya said to Gabrielle, "Thank you, Maman."

Gabrielle stayed silent for a moment, then said, "You're welcome, *ma petite chou*," no louder than a whisper, as she blinked back tears. Gaston became known as "Papa," and Jilberte was her "*soeur*," or sister.

* * *

Chaya talked about Rivka less and less as the year progressed, and the Delfosses rarely mentioned her, in fear that Chaya would become grief-stricken again over her mother's parting. Still, they thought often of Rivka, and kept in touch with her. How could they tell Chaya that her mother was only an hour away?

CHAPTER SIXTEEN

A New Identity

Rivka, September 1943

"Look up here," said Monsieur Hensler, staring tip-toed into his accordion-like lens.

Hensler's dwarfish stature required him to stand on a chair to meet Rivka at eye level, but his lack of height never compromised his extraordinary talents behind a camera. Rivka stood, solemn-faced, and peered toward the lens. A flash of blinding light illuminated the room, making her see spots as she blinked her eyes in the direction of Hensler's clean-shaven face.

"I'll develop the photo in my dark room and you'll be all set," he said, quietly putting his equipment back on the shelves.

Carl Hensler was a professional photographer and occasionally worked with Gaston at the local newspaper. He lived about an hour away in a village called Auderghem, in a tidy clapboard house bordering the lush Sonian Forest. Carl's wife, Marie, stood a foot taller than Carl, but was no longer fazed by it, having been his companion for so many years.

"His heart is bigger than anyone twice his size," Marie would say.

Carl regarded Gaston as both a mentor and friend, and knew that he would never ask anything of him unless it was truly important. When Gaston approached Carl with an enormous favor, he readily agreed. His wife, Marie, however, was not so sure.

"House a Jew? Are you serious?" she shrilled. "We could get killed for that!"

"Nonsense," reasoned Carl. "She will simply be our live-in housekeeper. Think of it this way, Marie—she'll be doing the cooking and cleaning."

"Okay, but just a few months," she agreed.

So Rivka became Carl and Marie's live-in housekeeper. With Gaston and Carl's help, Rivka obtained false identification papers. According to these documents, her name was "Bertha Lagaisse." They revealed nothing of her Jewish heritage, her Czech ancestry, or even her family.

Having grown up as the second oldest of ten kids, Rivka was adept at housekeeping. She could also sew, mend, cook, and garden. But what Carl loved most of all was Rivka's baking. Delicious scents of lemony sponge cake, warm apple strudel, and yeasty breads wafted through the two-story house, to Carl's great delight.

"It smells wonderful in here!" Carl would say. "You're going to make me burst a button from all your delicious food!"

Marie, however, was less forthcoming. While she enjoyed Rivka's cooking as much as Carl did, she was jealous of Rivka's talents. As a result, Marie was more likely to bark orders than offer words of praise.

"Remember to scrub the pots so they shine when you're done," she'd say after being served a hearty stew.

"I'd prefer you leave out the onions next time," she said, after eating nearly three portions of potato kugel.

Rivka knew better than to argue. With one slip of the tongue, she could easily be back on the streets.

Rivka kept to herself, staying as busy as possible. Whenever she paused to think about her family, a well of sadness flooded her. She prayed for her sisters and brothers, her parents, and of course, Zev and Chaya. While she couldn't actually communicate with anyone, she did speak softly to Chaya before she went to bed as she gazed at a tiny photo of her.

"I will come see you as soon as I can. I promise. I promise."

She wished Chaya could understand her reasons for leaving. Even more, she hoped someday Chaya could forgive her.

CHAPTER SEVENTEEN

The First Visit

Rivka, September 1944

Chaya at the Delfosse's farm

As the months went by, Chaya adapted to life with the Delfosses. She came to love Gabrielle and Gaston, and regarded them as family, having been little more than a toddler when she first arrived. Thoughts of Rivka, however, brought a mixture of love, sadness and confusion. Now four years old, Chaya barely recalled the day her mother left her, and didn't remember Zev at all. All she knew was that whenever she saw something that brought back memories of Rivka, a hollow ache filled her stomach. It was better not to think about her.

Rivka, on the other hand, thought of Chaya constantly, and wanted nothing more than to see her, if only for a day. After being away for nearly six months, she couldn't wait any longer.

"You'll be risking your life going out in the open like that," warned Carl. "You should stay here where you're safe."

Rivka stuck a photo of Chaya into her heavy wool coat. When it came to seeing her daughter, logic and reason took a back seat to longing and heartache.

"I have to see her," she said, wrapping a thick wool scarf around her neck.

"Are you crazy?" piped in Marie, who had come to care for Rivka despite her lingering jealousy.

"There are battles going on out there!" Soldiers were stationed throughout the area, and tanks were a frequent sight. Still, Rivka was determined.

"I have to see Chaya," Rivka said again. "I'll be back tonight."

Yes, it was winter, and the Delfosse's home was an hour away. Rivka could not board a train in fear of being caught, despite her illegal papers, and no one in the area owned a car. The only option was an old bicycle Carl found in the shed. It was long-neglected, but the frame was solid and it could take her where she needed to go.

Rivka hadn't ridden a bike since she was young, but it was faster than walking, and Wansin was a long ways away. Upon mounting, Rivka lost her balance and fell. She landed with a large thump, directly on her knee. Bits of gravel had lodged themselves into her skin and blood trickled down her leg. Her dress was ripped, and cold wind tore through the hole in her stockings. Still, Rivka did not turn back. Instead, she looked up, pointed her bike towards Auderghem, took a deep breath, and headed out.

While the roads were relatively flat, even the mildest uphill sent shooting pains through Rivka's injured knee. Still, she kept pedaling, breathing through the pain, thinking about Chaya and her sweet, dimpled face.

As she neared the Delfosse's house, Rivka looked up toward the road, and rode over a pothole. The sudden, jarring motion sent lightning bolts of pain to Rivka's knee, and she had to stop. She got off the bike, and looked at her leg. Her knee was swollen like a grapefruit.

Leaving the bike by the side of the road, Rivka dragged herself the rest of the way. She was less than a quarter mile, but it felt like eternity. Flushed, muddy, and nauseous from the pain, Rivka arrived at the Delfosse's doorstep.

"Mon dieu, Rivka!" moaned Gabrielle, "What happened to you?"

Gaston and Gabrielle gently lifted Rivka into the house, placed her on the sofa, and brought over some cold, wet rags and tincture.

"I fell off a bike," whispered Rivka, afraid that she'd be sick in the middle of the living room.

Chaya stood from the kitchen, looking stone-faced at her mother. She neither ran towards her nor shied away. She simply stared, clutching her doll, Bébé. Rivka turned toward Chaya, unable to move and opened her arms.

"Come here, Chaya! I've come all this way to see you. I've missed you so much!" Tears of happiness and relief at the sight of her healthy, beautiful daughter trailed down her dust-covered cheeks.

"Maman," Chaya whispered.

Rivka lifted her eyebrows, joyous to hear her name called. But Chaya's attention was turned to Gabrielle.

"Maman, may I please go outside?" said Chaya.

"No, we must stay here and visit with your mother. She came a very long way to see you," said Gabrielle as she turned Chaya toward Rivka.

Chaya clutched Gabrielle's leg.

"I don't want to. I want to go outside. Please, Maman."

Rivka felt her heart crumbling.

"It's okay," said Rivka, her voice barely above a whisper. "If she wants to play outside, that's fine," she added, forcing a smile.

Rivka assumed Chaya would be as overjoyed to see her as she was. Instead, Chaya wanted nothing to do with her. *All she remembers is me leaving her*, Rivka thought to herself. *To her, I'm the one who walked away...*

Rivka's mood changed as she looked out the window and saw Dowley the dog herding Chaya around the farm, running circles around her and gently nudging her with his nose. Chaya headed to the barn and went inside. When she came out, she was carrying one of the kittens. She brought it in the house and brought it to Rivka, who gently pet the tabby's soft, striped fur.

"She's soft," said Rivka. Chaya said nothing, but looked up and stared for a moment into Rivka's blue eyes.

"I'll bring him back," she said, turning to Gabrielle, and returned to the barn.

CHAPTER EIGHTEEN

A Brief Stay

Rivka, September 1944

Rivka and Chaya

"I don't know how you can get back to the Hensler's house," said Gaston, as dusk approached. "It's too far away for you to travel with your leg like that. I'll contact Carl and let him know."

Gaston looked at Rivka's knee, still painfully swollen and bruised.

"She'll need to stay here for a little while," said Gaston to Gabrielle.

The prospect was risky. Chaya was the only child hidden in Wansin, and there were certainly no adults in hiding. A farmer in a nearby village who had hidden three children had just been betrayed by a neighbor. He and his family were all taken away by the Nazis, along with the three children. None of them had returned.

"I will ask the Vankoeklebergs if you can stay with them while your knee heals," said Gaston to Rivka. "They have a daughter, Madeleine, who likes to play with Chaya. Maybe they can take you in."

The Vankoeklebergs lived on the next farm over, and while their house was not much bigger, they did have a modest guest room tucked in the back of the house where Rivka could safely hide. Gaston told them that while Rivka could not walk, she could sew to earn her keep. The Vankoeklebergs agreed to have her stay, but just until her knee was healed. They were kind, but also cautious, since they, too had heard about the farmer. Still, they'd grown to care for Chaya after seeing their daughter Madeleine play with her, and in turn, cared for Rivka, too.

Over the next several weeks, Rivka sewed curtains, duvet covers, and even playclothes for Madeleine. She hemmed dresses and pants, and darned socks. She had earned her keep and then some.

"Rivka!" said Madame Vankoekleberg, "You should rest and let your knee heal. You're going to go blind from all that sewing!"

But Rivka wanted to keep busy.

"What else do I have to do but sit around?" she said. "I might as well make myself useful." And she did. Her skill with a needle was impressive.

While Rivka remained hidden inside the house, she occasionally received visits from Gaston or Gabrielle with Chaya, who still called Gabrielle "Maman." Rivka suggested Chaya call her "*Tante*," meaning "aunt," so Chaya could distinguish between them.

As the swelling subsided, Rivka was able to put more weight on her knee and knew the time was coming when she would return to Auderghem. Rivka's fingers pushed in and out through the soft cotton cloth, the needle's rhythm helping her push away thoughts of Chaya—the person she loved the most in the world, knowing she would need to leave her yet again.

CHAPTER NINETEEN

Another Visit

Rivka, December 1944

Upon returning to the Hensler's house, Rivka received a warm welcome from both Carl and Marie.

"The house just wasn't the same without you!" smiled Carl, opening his arms towards the disheveled living room. Rivka returned with a heavy heart, but was thankful she had been able to see that her daughter was healthy and well cared for, and that she felt safe and welcomed at the Hensler's.

Soon Rivka was back into her routine as Carl and Marie's housekeeper, cooking, baking, cleaning, and sewing as she'd done before. Her knee had healed remarkably well. The only trace of her injury was the gravel marks that dotted her tender skin.

Rivka's recent visit to Wansin felt like a strange dream. *I can't stay away so long this time. My child is already forgetting me.*

Thoughts of visiting Chaya nagged at her. Rivka wanted more than anything to be back with her daughter. Guilt and remorse tore at her. *I am her mother. And yet I am here. Will she ever forgive me for leaving her? This was the only way...*

Sounds of gunfire no longer rattled her. They had become strangely normal, part of the background noise. A gray haze hovered above the skyline, remnants of gunpowder and smoke, truck exhaust, and smoldering fires.

Army vehicles drove through town, bearing flags from America, Canada, Great Britain, and of course, Germany. Soldiers' trucks were often parked haphazardly along roadsides, in front of taverns and shops. Rivka rarely ventured outside the Hensler's house, except to hang the wash on sunny days.

Despite all the signs of war, Rivka could not wait so long again to visit. One, two, then three months passed. The urge to see Chaya again nagged at her, like a deep ache from some unreachable place.

"Don't you hear what's going on outside, Rivka?" asked Carl, when Rivka shared her thoughts of paying another visit. An explosion rang in the distance, as if on cue.

"You see?" Carl said, pointing outside. Deaf to Carl's pleas, she prepared for her journey. The next morning, Rivka bid Carl and Marie farewell once more. They prayed for her safe return.

A fresh blanket of snow had fallen the previous night, cloaking the Belgian countryside in an expanse of bluish-white that shimmered in the dawn's gentle sunlight, masking the vestiges of war that lay hidden below. Billows of smoke from the previous night's gunfire left gray trails across the otherwise vibrant sky.

Rivka trudged through the layers of snow, crunching past the soft, fresh powder, into layers of snow and ice that had settled throughout the winter—cold, dense, and unforgiving. She walked slowly and deliberately, trying to avoid getting snow in her boots as she ventured into the knee-deep drifts. The wind whipped across her exposed skin, forcing her to cover her face with her scratchy wool scarf.

Rivka's nose ran and her eyes watered. Her forehead ached from the wind. The icy chill crept in, making its way to her fingers, her toes, her bones. Her body shivered beneath her dense fur coat. Still, she forged ahead.

The sounds of gunfire and bombing grew louder and louder. Tanks and army jeeps bearing flags from Canada, Great Britain, and the United States littered the road. There was not a civilian in sight.

Rivka had no choice but to walk toward the battleground; it was the only way to get to Wansin. Having walked this far, she was not about to turn back.

As she got closer and closer, she noticed some American soldiers approaching her. One aimed his rifle directly at her.

"What are you doing here?" he said in English.

Rivka did not understand, but she knew she had to think fast. She took out the photo of Chaya.

"This is my daughter," she said in French. "I am going to see her."

Rivka pointed to Chaya and tried to motion using body language that the girl in the photo was her daughter, then pointed across the field, toward Wansin.

"What's going on?" said another soldier standing nearby. "Who is this woman and what the hell is she doing here?"

"I think she must be a spy," whispered his comrade. "Why else would she be out in this God-forsaken weather in the middle of a war zone for Chrissakes?"

The soldiers shook their heads and laughed at Rivka, who stood in her elegant fur coat shivering before them.

One of the soldiers patted her down, making Rivka even more tense.

"No weapon. She's gotta be a spy. Let her go," he said. "She'll probably get killed by the Krauts anyhow."

The first soldier nodded to Rivka and lowered his gun.

"You sure you don't understand English? What if I were to tell you I was gonna put a bullet through your pretty little head right now, what would you say then?" he snickered.

Rivka remained expressionless. She held up Chaya's photo. "This is my daughter. I must go see her," she said again.

"Gotta give it to her," said the soldier to his buddy, "If she's faking it, she's a helluva good actress."

"Aw, leave her alone," said the other soldier. He knew his comrade had a mean streak, and it was better to send her off before things got messy. He stepped forward and motioned to Rivka,

"Go. *Allez!* Get outta here, okay?"

Rivka looked at him as he waved her away. There was both an urgency and kindness in his eyes.

A dizzying BOOM exploded dangerously close by, momentarily distracting the attending soldiers. Rivka tucked the photo back in her pocket, and ran as quickly as she could—away from the battlefield towards open farmland. She spotted a stone fence and ran alongside it, narrowly missing a spray of bullets.

Rivka veered as far as she could from the battlegrounds. She wandered through densely wooded fields, across frozen farmland, and towards the low-lying stone buildings she remembered from her last journey to Wansin. At last, she found a sign half-covered in snow, *"Bienvue en Wansin,"* and headed toward the square. She was almost there.

Exhausted, she trudged slowly but deliberately toward the Delfosse's house. A faint ray of sun cut through the winter clouds, casting a streak of yellow light across the Delfosse's weathered barn, and onto the small herd of thick-coated sheep in the adjacent pen. Rivka had just made her way through a war zone—unarmed and unharmed.

She arrived at the Delfosse's doorstep cold and wet, but otherwise completely unscathed. Nothing—not a snowstorm, an injured knee, or even a land battle would keep Rivka from visiting her daughter.

She tapped on the door.

"You look completely frozen!" said Gabrielle, welcoming Rivka in, and called to Jilberte to bring her a mug of hot tea.

"Come by the fire and warm up," said Gaston, who stoked the timber to a brilliant blue-orange blaze.

Gabrielle wrapped a warm wool blanket around Rivka's shoulders.

"Thank you," said Rivka, bringing her stiff, bone-chilled hands toward the hearth. Her mouth was so cold, she could barely speak.

Chaya looked up from her drawing to see who it was. Without another glance, she went back to her drawing.

"Aren't you going to say hello to your mother?" asked Gabrielle.

Chaya stared down at her picture, absent-mindedly doodling, pretending not to hear.

"Hello Chaya," said Rivka, coming over to greet Chaya. "I've come here to see you."

Chaya picked at the pencil, peeling off the wood.

"Hello," she said cooly, then walked to the kitchen to sharpen her pencil.

* * *

Chaya's behavior changed little the following day. She was distant but polite, though mature well beyond her years like so many other children of war. She knew Rivka was her mother, but Gabrielle was her Maman.

"You would never leave me like Tante did, right?" she once asked Gabrielle while getting ready for bed.

"No, I will never leave you," assured Gabrielle, wishing there was some way she could explain that Rivka had left Chaya because she loved her—not because she didn't.

"We can't expect a three-year-old to understand," said Gaston to Gabrielle sympathetically. "How could she?"

* * *

When Rivka said good-bye, Chaya waved, her other arm firmly wrapped around Gaston's leg. Gaston picked her up and put Chaya on his shoulders, then escorted Rivka to the gate.

"We'll see you next time," he said warmly.

"Thanks again for taking such good care of Chaya," said Rivka. She looked up at her daughter, took her little hand in hers, and kissed it gently. "See you soon, *mamela*."

Together, Gaston and Chaya watched Rivka make her way down the dirt road. This time Rivka turned around to wave good-bye.

CHAPTER TWENTY

A Picnic With Gaston

Chaya, December 1944

Gaston

"Let's go for a bike ride," said Gaston after Rivka left.

Chaya's eyes lit up. She loved going on his special tandem bike.

"One seat for me and one for you," he said the first time he showed her his two-person bicycle, as though it was the only one in the world, made especially for them. Chaya had never seen anything like it. Gaston tied strips of green, pink and yellow fabric on her handlebars.

"Look, Papa!" Chaya would exclaim, as the wind blew them skyward. "They're flying!"

Gaston did most of the pedaling, of course, but Chaya's feet spun around and around until they were too tired. She would then line up both of her little feet on the center bar and hold on to the handlebars and take in the view. Trees, houses, farms, and animals all became a colorful blur. The first time they'd gone for a ride, Chaya's thick, wavy hair was so wind-blown, she could barely see.

"You look like one of my sheep!" laughed Gaston when he saw her. Gabrielle made sure she braided Chaya's hair after that.

"Now you won't have your hair blowing in your eyes," said Gabrielle, tying each braid with a green satin ribbon.

Chaya's eyes watered as they cut through the cold winter air. Tanks had rolled through the center of town, flattening the snow with their heavy, rolling treads. Gaston had shown Chaya how to identify the nationality of the army vehicles scattered around town by the colors of their flags.

"Is that from America, Papa?" asked Chaya, looking at a truck with a small emblem in red, white, and blue.

"That's from England, Chaya. American flags are red, white, and blue, too, but with lots of stars and stripes. I'll draw you a picture of one when we get home."

Chaya had met an American soldier once. He had kindly offered her a stick of chewing gum.

"Look what I can do," he said, and made a bubble. Rather than delight her, the popping sound terrified Chaya, especially when he continued to crack small bubbles between his teeth.

"*Non, merci,*" said Chaya shyly, backing away. She didn't want to chew something that exploded.

Gaston looked back at a tank. This one had a flag with red intersecting arms—a swastika—the symbol of Germany's Nazi regime.

"What's that?" asked Chaya.

"That is a sign that means ready, set, go!" said Gaston. With the Germans in town, it was time to hide.

He pointed to a railroad car that was slowly ambling on its tracks to divert her attention.

"Let's race the train!" said Gaston.

They biked as quickly as they could for a mile or so, then turned right and parked the bike just outside a deserted office. It had been used by the local newspaper agency until the war broke out. Metal file drawers were pushed together in rows like soldiers standing at attention.

"Look what I have," said Gaston, reaching into his deep coat pockets.

From one, he pulled out a rumpled paper sack. Inside were two rolls and a small wedge of cheese. From the other pocket he removed two squares of wrapped chocolate—a rare treat.

"I think it's time for a picnic!" said Gaston.

Chaya took Gaston's hand and went inside. It was dingier than Gaston had remembered, but was a fine respite from the Nazis who had rolled into Wansin that morning. How long they would be there was anybody's guess. Gaston was relieved they had gotten away in time, and that Chaya had not noticed.

"She's got eyes like a hawk," Gabrielle often said. "She picks up on everything."

Gaston found a roll of newsprint and spread it like a blanket across the cold, musty floor. He spotted a stub of a pencil lying atop a dusty shelf and gave it to Chaya.

"I think we need to make our tablecloth fancy, don't you? How about you draw some flowers on it."

Chaya loved to draw and immediately took to task. When she was done, she said, "I made a flower for you, Papa, and one for Maman and Jilberte and Dowley, too."

"Then I shall make one for you," replied Gaston, and drew her a rose.

"That's a pretty flower," she said admiringly.

"Do you know how to spell 'flower'?" he asked.

"No," said Chaya. "I don't know how to spell anything."

"Then I'll show you," he said, and took her hand, and together spelled her first word: *fleur*.

"But first things first, *mademoiselle*. You need to learn how to spell your own name."

Gaston wrote out Chaya's name in large block letters, then showed her how to grasp a pencil and trace over them. She wrote her name again and again.

"How's this Papa?" she asked.

"*Magnifique!*" said Gaston.

Chaya swelled with pride.

As they ate their rolls and cheese, Gaston told Chaya about his most recent adventure with Dowley, adding a few dramatic flourishes.

"When one of our sheep got loose, do you know what Dowley did? He circled it until it faced the pen, then bit it right on the bum! The sheep went running back into their pen and that was that!"

The image of Dowley chomping a sheep's bottom made Chaya giggle. She smiled with a mouthful of bread.

Gaston wiped a crumb off Chaya's grinning face and said, "Are we ready for dessert?"

Chaya nodded. Gaston broke a piece of chocolate in two and handed one to Chaya.

"Mmmm," she said, savoring it.

They played tic-tac-toe using the pencil stub and made silly animals out of random shapes. Before they left, they shared the other chocolate square.

"Well, I guess that's the last of our picnic supplies," said Gaston, hearing a truck roar by. He hoped it was a sign the Nazis had cleared out. "Shall we head home?"

The roads were eerily quiet as they pedaled back to Wansin. Gaston kept his eyes on the road and listened for signs. In the distance he could hear gunshots, but they sounded like they were coming from the other direction. Still, he rode faster, hoping to get back home before dark. Winter roads froze at night, making it hard to navigate by bicycle, especially with Chaya in tow.

When they got home, Gabrielle greeted Chaya with a big hug.

"Welcome home, *ma chère!* Where have you been?" said Gabrielle.

"We had a picnic!" said Chaya excitedly.

Her cheeks were bright pink. Gabrielle grasped them with her warm hands.

"Let's get you some warm milk, okay?" and led her to the kitchen.

While Chaya sipped her milk, Gabrielle took her passport from the pocket of her housecoat and stuck it back in her bureau. She was thankful to be the only one home when the German soldiers knocked on the door.

CHAPTER TWENTY-ONE

A Close Call

Chaya, January 1945

Gabrielle herding sheep at her small farm in Hannut, Belgium

Even as the snow piled higher, Chaya and Madeleine ventured outside, playing hide-and-go-seek, swinging into drifts of freshly fallen snow, and visiting the farm animals. When the weather got too cold, they would go inside the Delfosse's barn and warm up in the company of the resident cats.

The girls were nearly four, but they had developed an awareness as sharp as any adult. They could distinguish between fighter planes and rockets, and knew where and how to protect themselves if needed. So when a whistling sound whirred across the sky one afternoon, Chaya and Madeleine ran for cover, arms overhead. They huddled together behind a snow-covered pile of wood, hearts beating wildly. When the explosions faded, they looked at each other and silently bid one another good-bye, then ran back to their respective houses as fast as their little legs could carry them.

Incidents like these were just a part of everyday life. This was all Chaya knew—or at least all she could remember. Even so, she was happy living with Gabrielle and Gaston, who loved and protected her, no matter what was going on in the outside world.

There was one time, however, that Gaston learned the Nazis were headed into Wansin. It was too late to make a plan, too late for a "picnic." They had to act fast.

"We have to hide," said Gaston to Gabrielle, motioning to Chaya.

"Come, Chaya, we must go to the cellar right now," he explained, "And we must be very, very quiet, okay?" Chaya looked at Gaston, wide-eyed, and completely serious. Without further explanation, she instinctively knew. This was not a game of hide-and-seek, but a matter of life and death.

Gaston, Gabrielle and Chaya ran to the dirt cellar and closed the door overhead. The place smelled of mold and root vegetables and fermenting hops and earth, but it was the safest place to hide. No one dared breathe as a soldier's shadow descended overhead. With the butt of his rifle, they could hear him trying to break the latch open. Chaya held her breath. Her heart sounded so loud in her ears, she was sure the soldier would hear her. She pursed her lips together and glued her arms against her sides, trying to be as still as a statue. Bam! Bam! Bam! Splinters of wood rained overhead.

The door began to buckle. One crack, then two. Gaston took Chaya's hand and squeezed it, then held her close. Gabrielle grasped the rosary beads around her neck, praying silently.

Just as the door was about to buckle, a faraway voice called in German, "What are you doing over there? Looking for liquor again? Get away from there!"

With that, the pounding sound stopped. They could hear the soldier walking away.

Gabrielle, Gaston, and Chaya took a collective breath. *Was he really gone? Would he come back?* All three listened for activity overhead. They could hear the soldiers walking around, slamming doors, taking orders, laughing. Finally, they heard the chug of a truck's engine and the soldiers getting in. Only after they were long gone did Gaston dare open the cellar door.

"Stay down there while I look around," Gaston whispered to Gabrielle.

He climbed out of the cellar and saw deep, rugged tire tracks across his front lawn. The front door remained wide open, as were the cupboards. "Pigs," muttered Gaston upon seeing the mess they'd made. The entry, kitchen, and hallway were marked with a maze of muddy boot prints. The kitchen looked like it had been ransacked. Luckily they hadn't taken any valuables; they were obviously just looking for food and drink.

"Well, they certainly helped themselves," said Gaston as he went to get Gabrielle and Chaya. "We have a bit of cleaning up to do, but at least they're gone."

"*Mon dieu!* Who do these people think they are?" said Gabrielle.

Chaya watched Gabrielle as she walked around the house. She bent down to pick up a broken dish and nearly slipped in a puddle of water from a broken vase.

"I can help you Maman," she said, and went to get the broom. She came back carrying the middle of the wooden handle, and began to sweep. Gabrielle smiled as she watched Chaya, her little hands wrapped around the tall wooden broomstick.

"Thank you, *mon petit chou.* How about you just come here and sit with me for a minute? The mess can wait."

Gabrielle leaned forward and rubbed her forehead, then sat up and grasped her rosary beads. She mouthed the words to Our Father, one of the prayers Chaya had learned while living with the Delfosses.

"Thank you God, for sparing us," Gabrielle whispered.

Chaya carried the broom toward Gabrielle, then leaned it against the table. She sat on Gabrielle's lap, resting her head beneath Gabrielle's chin.

Together they sat for a long time, half-sleeping, savoring the silence.

CHAPTER TWENTY-TWO

The Escape

Zev, January 1945

While the Delfosses hid beneath the ground, so, too, did Chaya's father, Zev. He and his friend, Sandik, a fellow inmate at Buchenwald lay buried under piles of leaves to remain unseen. They had made a narrow escape from the camp only days before.

Zev and Sandik were digging ditches just outside the camp's gates, and noticed the guards wandering off-site, smoking cigarettes and chatting. They took advantage of the moment and walked backwards a few steps, testing to see if the guards turned around, but they just kept talking. Zev and Sandik looked at one another, signaled the exit as though they'd planned this forever, and made a run for it. They ran across the dirt road, and hid behind a row of houses, then headed to the nearby forest and ran until their weakened lungs gave out. Luckily the snow was nearly melted, and piles of dried leaves still clung to the ground. They buried themselves beneath the leaves to stay hidden as they slept.

Both men had arrived at Buchenwald on the same truck the previous year, and ended up bunking together in the barracks. They were amazed to discover that not only did both their families come from small towns near the Carpathian mountains, they had also both moved to Belgium, just miles from one another.

Despite the constant torment of starvation and physical exhaustion at the camps, a glimmer of hope is what kept Zev and Sandik going day after wretched day. Giving up would have been easy. Getting up every morning was far more difficult. When the will to live dried up, that was the end. They had witnessed this time and again.

Like Zev, Sandik also had a young child, a son they called Uli, who was about five years old. His wife was from The Netherlands and had moved to Belgium after Sandik found work there as a stone mason. He was slighter than Zev, though remarkably strong for his size. With his blue-gray eyes, wavy brown hair, and angular features, he had been a handsome man by any standard. But after spending years in the camps, he had become as emaciated, worn and weary as everyone else.

Starving and filthy, Zev and Sandik had to travel by night. If their hollow appearance didn't give them away, their striped uniforms surely would. They managed to reach Sandik's apartment after traveling for several days. The front door was locked, but Sandik remembered a window around the side that would allow them access inside.

There was no hot water, but a rusty trickle gurgled out of the kitchen faucet, allowing the men to wash some of the dirt from their faces and hands. Sandik and Zev changed into fresh clothes that had been tucked in a drawer. They were so baggy, the men had to wrap yarn through their belt loops to prevent them from falling off. They smiled at how ridiculous they looked, but at least the clothes were clean. As he discarded his worn, tattered uniform, Zev felt like a weight had been lifted. He was finally free.

Eager to hear of the whereabouts of his family, Sandik learned that his family friend, Lieke, was still living nearby. She was Catholic, of Dutch descent, with cropped blond hair, now streaked with white. Like Zev's friend Louis, she had promised to do her best to keep track of Sandik's family. Through a series of underground messages, she had learned that both Sandik's wife and son had perished in the camps.

Telling this news to Sandik was painstaking for her.

"I'm so sorry," she said, crying into her handkerchief.

She took Sandik's hand and placed something in his palm.

"She wanted me to hold this for you," she said, "In case you came back."

Sandik didn't need to open his hand to know what it was. He knew the feeling of his wife's gold locket without looking. He had given it as a gift on their son's first birthday.

Sandik stood there, stricken. His knees buckled and he sat where he'd fallen like a maimed animal, staring at nothing with wide, vacant eyes. He held the locket and opened it. A well of tears blurred his vision as he gazed at the tiny photographs of his wife and child.

The shock of this news drained the last vestiges of hope that had kept Sandik going all those years.

"I have nothing left. Nothing," he told Zev mournfully.

Zev tried in vain to reassure him, but there was nothing he could say. Sandik had seen his brothers and father perish at the camps, and gathered that his mother and sisters had suffered the same fate. All he had left were his wife and child, and now they, too, were gone.

Sandik sat on the bed he had once shared with his wife.

"I need to close my eyes," he told Zev and lay down to rest. He didn't even bother to take off his shoes.

Zev left him alone, knowing there was nothing he could do or say.

"Yes, rest is the best thing," he said to Zev, and gently closed the door.

When Zev came to wake up Sandik the next morning, he remained fast asleep. He looked like he was dreaming, smiling even. Normally a light sleeper, he remained eerily still.

"It's almost nine, Sandik," said Zev, from across the room.

As he came closer, however, he knew. Sandik's skin was nearly gray and clammy, his lips a deep purplish-blue. Zev checked Sandik's pulse and tried to revive him, to no avail.

Shocked, Zev felt a wave of heat then blacked out, smacking his head on the wood floor as he fell. When the dizziness subsided, he sat by the bed and stared at his friend. *I should have stayed with you, Sandik. I'm so sorry. I'm so sorry.* Zev sat there unmoving, feeling like his body was made of lead.

Knowing he could not stay there, Zev arose and covered his friend's face with a sheet, then recited the Mourner's Kaddish.

"*Yitgadal, v'yitkadash, sh'may rabah...* Rest in peace, my dear friend," said Zev between tears. "I hope you can see your family wherever you are now." Weakened by sorrow, his voice was little more than a hoarse whisper.

Zev found some shoes to put on and headed to the door. As he left, he washed his hands and face with the few remaining trickles of rusty water, then kissed the mezuzah that was still mounted to the sagging door frame and closed the door without looking back.

Without another thought, he headed towards Antwerp to find Louis, who had promised to watch out for Rivka and Chaya. *I hope he has kept his word,* thought Zev. *Please God, let me not suffer the same fate as Sandik.*

CHAPTER TWENTY-THREE

Back at the Camps

Zev, January 1945

After walking all day, Zev found an abandoned barn to spend the night. Exhausted, he tried to sleep, but struggled to escape the shackle of recent memories. Images too powerful to repress launched themselves at him like grenades, one more disturbing than the next. Then he thought of his dear friend Sandik, unmoving. *If only I stayed with him. Maybe he'd still be alive. If only...*

After surviving nearly three years in concentration camps, Zev had seen far too many families just like his, brought in like cattle awaiting slaughter. The children were always the first to "take a shower." The possibility of being captured and taken back to the camps still haunted him.

Zev had survived bouts of slave labor in both Bergen-Belsen and Auschwitz before being transferred to Buchenwald. He managed to avoid the gas chambers because he could work for twelve-hour stretches without complaint. Silently, painfully, he dug ditches, repaired makeshift barracks, cleaned latrines, and built officer's quarters as guards stood at attention, their trained German Shepherds snarling at even the faintest hint of eye contact.

At his lowest point, Zev wondered what the purpose was of laboring in the camps day after day if all his loved ones were already gone. Zev walked toward the fence, and without anyone seeing, quickly tossed the blanket over the electrified barbed wired fence. *It should only take a moment, and then it will all be over.*

As his hand neared the fence, an image entered his mind—that of Chaya smiling up at him. Zev hadn't seen her since she was a baby, but it was definitely her. In his mind, he could see a young girl with long blond braids, and the same sparkling hazel eyes he remembered. *Maybe she's alive. Maybe this is a sign.*

Zev reached for the blanket and pulled it off the fence. If there was even a sliver of hope that he would see his wife and daughter again, he decided he would keep going. He would not give up.

"Please God," he prayed, "I don't need to live forever, just long enough to see my daughter married." The dream of being at Chaya's wedding became Zev's greatest wish.

Zev woke up and looked around, hoping to find a softer spot to sleep than the hard, cold barn floor. He found some dry hay and made a bed for himself.

As he closed his eyes, he thought of Chaya. An image of her long, flaxen braids, dimpled cheeks and bright hazel eyes slowly entered his mind, just as it had when he was in the camps. He smiled, took a deep breath, and felt his body relax for the first time in a very, very long while. *I want to live to see her again.* Within moments, he was fast asleep.

CHAPTER TWENTY-FOUR

At Louis' at Last

Zev, January 1945

The journey from Sandik's house to Louis's was not far in miles, but it seemed much longer as Zev headed there alone. He thought about his friend and the possibility that his news would likely be the same. Losing Sandik was yet another blow to his already fragile spirit, and Zev knew that he, too, could not take much more.

As Zev walked down Louis' street, it was clear that the war had gotten the best of this once-charming neighborhood. Buildings struck by bombs looked like injured prey, their interiors exposed to the sharp claws of winter. German flags adorned with red-and-white swastikas no longer hung proudly, but drooped at odd angles, exaggerating their fraying ends.

Louis' home, however, looked just as he remembered it. The painted evergreen shutters were peeling, and the front door had a splintered hole where the shiny brass knocker used to be, but otherwise Louis' sturdy brick home remained the same as ever. Zev pounded softly on the front door. No answer. He waited and knocked again. *Perhaps he's not home*, Zev thought, and turned around to leave.

"Who is it?" yelled a woman in Flemish, her quick, light footsteps approaching the entry.

"It's me, Zev," he said, turning back around.

The heavy wooden door opened, and a woman no taller than Zev's shoulder peered out. It was Louis' wife, Camille. Her flecked amber eyes opened wide as it dawned on her who the man was standing at her door.

"Zev?" she said in disbelief. "Oh my gosh, Zev! Please, come in!"

She looked up at Zev.

"You look like you've seen the devil," she said, shocked at his appearance.

Zev smiled at the expression.

"Ah, that's a good way of putting it, Camille. Yes, I most certainly have."

Camille stood there, frozen. Zev knew she only half believed that he was actually who he said he was, Louis' old, dear friend.

With his shaved head and sunken cheeks, Zev bore little resemblance to the lively, strapping fellow he'd been before the war. The person Camille had known was filled with joy and laughter. He was now somber, spent, hollow. Still, Zev's hazel eyes still shone with kindness and warmth.

"Let me fix you something," said Camille, welcoming Zev inside.

Camille took Zev's arm as though aiding an elder, and walked him towards the dining room.

"Louis should be home soon."

The house was as tidy as ever, though it was darker than before the war. Heavy upholstery fabric now covered all the street-facing windows, blocking out the sunlight.

Zev looked at the makeshift drapery.

"We put them up a couple of years ago," said Camille.

"Soldiers started looking inside the house and coming in whenever they felt like it. They seemed to think they could just help themselves to food, liquor, even my mother's crystal. One of them decided he liked the brass knocker and pulled it right off. I covered the front windows so the soldiers couldn't look inside anymore."

"Do they still come by?" asked Zev, concerned.

"Ah, no," answered Camille. "The Gestapo finally left town a few months ago. I just never got around to taking the coverings down—just in case. It is rather dark in here, but I've gotten used to it."

Camille went to stir something bubbling up in a large soup pot.

"It smells good," said Zev, inhaling the wafting aroma.

"Oh, it's just soup," said Camille modestly, "A few vegetables from the garden and the like. You're certainly welcome to have some." She blew on the wooden spoon and tasted it, then added some salt. "It's almost done."

Zev noticed his reflection from a mirror as he faced the dining table. He couldn't believe that was actually him, but it was all too familiar a sight, especially after surviving not one but three labor camps. Zev could see the outline of his skull, his sinewy neck, and a crescent-shaped scar behind his ear. He turned his body away from the mirror.

"Can I bring you something to drink?" she asked.

"Yes, please," said Zev politely.

Camille ladeled soup into a shallow bowl and brought it to the table. He gazed at the soup as if he were just given a bounty of treasure.

"Eat while it's warm," said Camille, and handed him a piece of freshly baked bread, which Zev accepted graciously.

He inhaled the heavenly aroma as he said the *hamotze*. *Thank you God for this bread…*

Most of the food doled out to Jews at the camps—if they were fed at all—was often rotten, moldy, or ridden with maggots. Zev hadn't eaten a fresh, home-cooked meal since the night he was taken from his home.

"Thank you so much, Camille," said Zev, looking down at the swirl of steam rising like a tiny tornado from his bowl. He blew on the broth and sipped it slowly.

"This is absolutely delicious," said Zev.

His malnourished palate exaggerated the flavors of the vegetables. He savored the sweet carrots, the buttery potatoes, the hearty beans and nutty barley. Zev wanted to tell Camille that it was truly the best meal he'd eaten in a very long while. It might've been just a peasant's meal to Camille, but for Zev, it was heavenly.

Camille brought a small bowl of soup to the table for herself, and together, they ate silently, waiting for Louis to come home. Just as Camille was clearing the bowls, Louis approached the front door. She placed the dishes by the sink, wiped her hands on her apron, and hurried toward the entry.

"Hello, my dear!" said Louis, and gave her a kiss on the cheek. "We have a visitor!" she announced, then whispered. "Zev is here, Louis. He made it back. Can you believe it? After all this time..." She rattled on nervously, "I already gave him some soup. He's clearly starved—just skin and bones."

* * *

Louis looked down the hallway toward the dining room. He saw a man with a shaven head, wearing a heavy jacket that looked as ridiculous as a boy trying on his father's suit. *Could this really be him?* The Zev he knew had broad, muscular shoulders, a tall, straight back, and a thatch of thick, glossy black hair—a far cry from the shrunken stranger who slouched at the table.

As Louis walked toward the dining room, he gently inquired, "Zev?"

Zev turned around. He stood up, holding onto the chair's back, and smiled.

"Louis, my friend. It's good to see you."

He extended his bony hand to Louis, who stepped forward and hugged him tightly.

"I'm so thankful you're here," said Louis, his voice cracking as a well of emotions constricted his throat. "When I hadn't heard from you for so long, I figured...I didn't think you'd...." His voice trailed off, unable to say the words aloud.

* * *

Zev noticed that Louis had changed little since he'd last seen him. Zev hadn't thought about his appearance in the camps. Everyone was the same—shorn, starved, and dressed in stripes. Since escaping, he'd become more self-conscious, aware of how different he seemed.

The men stared at each other.

"You look well," said Zev.

"You've looked better," said Louis, smiling, then added, "Nothing a little rest and a lot of Rivka's cooking won't cure."

"You've seen her then?" asked Zev, his heart now racing.

"It's been a long time since I've had her famous sponge cake, but yes," said Louis. He noticed the vein pulsating across Zev's temple, his fist tensely clenched around the fabric napkin.

"Yes, Zev, of course I contacted her. I promised you I would." Louis was nothing if not a man of his word.

He took out a small cigar box in his kitchen cabinet and showed Zev the notes and the matchbooks, the writing now blurred, edges frayed.

"She stayed at the old warehouse for awhile, until your daughter got sick. You remember how bitter cold it gets there," he said.

Zev's stomach clenched.

"Chaya got sick?" he worried.

Louis paused, clearly trying to sort out his thoughts. Zev interpreted this silence as the calm before the storm.

"She didn't make it, did she?" he whispered, barely audible.

Louis scooted his chair a bit closer and put his arm around Zev's shoulders. "They're okay Zev. Both of them. They're safe," he said reassuringly.

Zev's face softened and blood flushed to his cheeks. His hand unclenched, and he seemed to sink into his chair, as though his bones had suddenly melted.

"Oh! Thank God!" he exclaimed. His relief was palpable.

As he took a deep breath, Zev straightened up and smiled, eyes glistening with tears.

"They're okay," he said aloud. "Thank God!" he exclaimed again, clasping his hands together. He smiled and put his face over his eyes, now openly sobbing. "I'm sorry...I'm just happy," he said, then started laughing, both from relief and self-consciousness. "I'm just so happy!"

Louis laughed with him. "They are luckier than most, my friend. Very lucky indeed."

Louis continued, "Rivka is staying about an hour from here in Auderghem. I'll take you to her. She knows how to get to where your daughter is staying, with a family in Wansin."

As Louis explained what he knew about Rivka and Chaya, Zev's mind spun. He watched Louis talk, and yet he had a hard time focusing on anything but the fact that his daughter and wife had survived. *They are alive! My Chaya and Rivka are alive!* He could barely contain himself.

"How soon can we see them?" asked Zev, interrupting Louis as he explained how he connected Rivka to the Delfosse family through the hospital nun.

Sensing Zev's restlessness, Louis said, "How about now?"

Camille packed up some bread and cheese, and found a hat to warm Zev's shaved head. Louis brought him a leather belt, some extra clothes and sundries, and stuffed them into a drawstring sack. Within minutes, they were on their way to Auderghem.

CHAPTER TWENTY-FIVE

An Extraordinary Reunion

Zev, January 1945

Louis and Zev got into Louis' truck, the old gray pick-up they had used for the moving business so many years ago. The scene was familiar— Louis driving, Zev in the passenger seat. The truck still had its old, musty smell, its chugging engine. The same tattered wool blanket lay spread across the back seat. And yet, nothing was the same.

Zev looked out the window. The synagogue he had once attended, with its beautiful stained glass and domed ceilings was completely destroyed. A ragged stone wall was all that remained of this once glorious building. Store-fronts greeted passersby with "Closed" signs and broken windows. Even the post office was boarded up. Piles of water-stained letters waited hopefully by the front door.

As they headed out of town, Zev thought about Rivka. He hadn't seen her for nearly three years.

Zev had grown up in the same small, rural village as Rivka's family. He knew her sisters and brothers, her parents, nieces, and nephews. He wondered, with a heavy heart, who, if anyone, had survived. Zev feared Rivka's family had suffered the same fate as his own. His mind strayed, dreaming about those he had lost.

Louis drove over a huge pothole, sending Zev nearly flying out of his seat.

"That's one way to wake you up!" joked Louis, noticing Zev's half-closed eyes bolting open.

"Yes, and good thing, too," said Zev.

He looked out and was greeted with an endless pasture, now scattered with patches of snow and neatly harvested rows of soil. A sign bearing a sunflower peeked out from behind the fence. It reminded him of all the train rides he'd taken with Rivka, traveling past endless fields of sunflowers, a blur of golden yellow. Zev's heart raced knowing he would soon reunite with his beloved wife.

As they approached Auderghem, Zev broke into a cold sweat. A wave of self-consciousness poured over him, a sensation he hadn't felt since he was a boy. Zev gazed down at his bony arms, his filthy, overgrown nails, the string of soot-black numbers inscribed in his skin. *I look awful.* He ran his fingers across the stubble on his scalp, and put the hat back on.

Louis noticed Zev trying in vain to spruce himself up and said reassuringly, "Rivka won't care what you look like, Zev. Believe me," said Louis. "She'll just be glad to see you," and patted Zev gently on his scrawny leg.

Louis slowed the truck and parked a few houses away from the Hensler's house. "It's that one over there," said Louis, "The one with the woman in the yard."

He pointed to the second to the last house on the street. Zev took a deep breath and looked up.

"Do you want me to go with you?" asked Louis.

"No. I'm okay," said Zev unconvincingly. "Thanks so much for taking me, Louis."

"I'll wait until you go in anyhow," said Louis. "Just in case."

Zev thanked Louis again and bid him good-bye. He walked slowly down the street and stopped in front of the house, taking it in. A woman in a floppy, straw sun hat was working out front, pulling weeds.

"Can I help you?" she asked, squinting towards the sun.

"I'm looking for Rivka. Rivka Slomovich? I was told she's staying here."

"What do you want with her?" asked Marie defensively.

She stood up and adjusted her large-brimmed hat, then crossed her arms suspiciously. "Rivka didn't say she was expecting anyone."

Zev walked a few steps closer.

"I'm her husband," he said.

"Pardon?" said Marie, not quite absorbing the news. "What did you just say?" she asked.

"I'm Zev, Rivka's husband," he repeated.

Marie's face softened as this extraordinary news dawned on her.

"*Oh mijn God!*" she said, taking off her gardening gloves and wrapping her free hand around Zev's shoulders. "Welcome! Rivka will be so happy to see you!" She headed towards the front door. "Please come in!"

"Rivka! Rivka!" yelled Marie through the house.

"Why are you yelling, Marie?" said Carl. "Rivka's out in back, hanging laundry," he said to Marie, then looked up at the slight figure leaning against the doorway. "May I help you?" said Carl.

"This is Rivka's husband, Zev," smiled Marie, and introduced him to Carl.

"Rivka's husband?" said Carl with a mixture of confusion and excitement.

"That Zev? You look so much different than in the picture!" he said.

"Ah, yes. I don't know which picture you mean, but I imagine I do," said Zev, self-consciously scratching his shaven head. He was so overwhelmed with anticipation he could barely stand.

Zev could see Rivka heading toward him, holding a fresh pile of linens, blocking him from view.

"What is it, Marie?" asked Rivka, "I was out in the backyard."

"You have a special guest, Rivka," said Marie, and signaled for Zev.

He stepped forward and smiled. "Rivka," was all he could think to say.

"Zev?" she said, half-wondering if she was dreaming.

He walked up and hugged Rivka, trying not to break down. "I've come—for you and Chaya."

Rivka stood there, shocked, her pile of neatly folded sheets tilting like a lopsided smile, then falling in a silent heap to the floor.

"I thought you were...I didn't know what to think anymore," she whispered, not moving.

"I just got out," said Zev, "from the camps. Louis took me here." He stepped forward and took both her hands. They were warmed from the sun and felt good in his. Zev looked into Rivka's dusk-blue eyes, now glazed with tears. She smiled and looked at her husband. *You are so beautiful, my Rivka. So very beautiful.*

"How about we sit down and have some tea?" asked Carl.

Marie brought some biscuits and jam to the table, followed by steaming cups of coffee. Both Zev and Rivka sat in a haze, staring at each other, then looked down shyly, as though they were teenagers again.

Zev could tell by Rivka's expression that the sight of his starved frame, sunken cheeks and shaved head was unsettling. But he hoped that once she looked at his eyes, that she would see past that. He suddenly felt the release of an enormous weight, one he'd unknowingly carried with him every day for nearly three years. Zev inhaled deeply, trying to hold back tears.

"We know you want to go see your daughter," said Carl to Zev. "But you don't need to leave right now, do you? We'd like to give your lovely wife a proper goodbye."

"How about you stay the night so Rivka can pack up and you can relax a bit?" said Marie.

"Good idea," said Carl. "Rest up, Zev. We can give you a ride to the train station tomorrow morning."

Rivka and Zev looked at one another and silently agreed.

"Yes," said Zev, "That would be nice. Thank you."

Zev was exhausted, both physically and emotionally, and spent most of the afternoon resting.

* * *

Rivka finished straightening up and then pulled out her suitcase from under the bed. There really wasn't much to pack—the valuables that she had stuffed into the weather-beaten case had long ago been traded for food on the black market. Still, she patiently folded her garments, then pored over the handful of photographs, tucked beneath a tear in the fabric lining.

Rivka looked at a photo of Zev, one that captured his easy grin and handsome features—the way he looked before the war. With some much-needed nourishment, he would look like his old self again. But Zev seemed different now, subdued. Rivka knew, however, that she, too, was no longer the same person she'd been before the war began.

She finished packing and brought another load of laundry to dry outside. Rather than return inside, she spread out a blanket and sat on a bench, tilting her face towards the fading sun.

CHAPTER TWENTY-SIX

Back Together Again

Rivka, February 1945

"She probably won't remember me," said Zev anxiously, as they exited the train to Hannut.

"Well, she hasn't seen you since she was a baby," said Rivka.

Zev's face fall, clearly concerned.

"You're her father, Zev. She'll know," said Rivka, backpedaling, though she, too, was filled with doubt.

Rivka didn't tell Zev that she, too, had become little more than a visitor. No longer was she "Mama," but a more distant "Tante." Her visits had been met with little more than politeness, as if she were someone to be tolerated rather than embraced. Rivka knew that Chaya would not remember Zev, but it would only hurt him to admit the truth. Admitting it to herself was hard enough.

* * *

Chaya, now nearly five, regarded Gabrielle and Gaston as her parents. They loved her, fed her, and kept her safe. They treated her like a daughter, and she responded in kind.

Chaya had come to enjoy waking up to the sound of Gaston and Dowley herding the sheep and Gabrielle humming while she cooked breakfast. She liked visiting Madeleine next door and going on bike rides with Gaston. She also loved exploring the farm, especially the kittens up in the barn. After living at the Delfosse's house for a year, this was her home, the longest she'd lived anywhere.

Chaya planned to stay at the Delfosse's house forever. She was happy there. She was loved. The last thing she expected was for two strangers to return and take her away from the place she called home—even if they were her parents.

* * *

"We have the chance to start over again," said Rivka hopefully.

"It'll be okay, Zev. You'll see."

She said this as much for herself as she did for Zev, as they stepped off the train platform, gathered their things, and headed towards town.

The walk from the train to the Delfosse's was tiring for Zev, and by the time they arrived, Zev had to lean on the door to steady himself. Rivka stepped forward and knocked on the door.

"Who is it?" shouted Gabrielle from the other end of the house as she shuffled toward the door.

"It's me, Rivka," said Rivka, then added, "Zev is here with me," but her voice was drowned out by the rustle of excitement coming from inside.

Rivka could hear Gabrielle shouting to Gaston, "*Quelle surprise!* Rivka is here!" as the click-click-click of her heeled shoes trailed toward the door.

"Welcome!" said Gabrielle, warmly embracing Rivka, then noticed that there was, in fact, someone with her.

"My name is Zev," said Zev to Gabrielle. "I am Chaya's father."

CHAPTER TWENTY-SEVEN

A Bittersweet
Return

Chaya, February 1945

"Who is that man?" whispered Chaya, pointing to a gaunt figure by the door. She cowered behind Gabrielle.

"He is your father, Chaya," she said softly.

Chaya stared in disbelief, then panicked. *That can't be true. No, he is at the wrong house,* Chaya thought. *I already have a father.* She looked up at Gaston for reassurance, but he merely patted her head, then smiled at the stranger by the door and walked toward him.

Chaya inched toward Gabrielle. She looked at her with a sad smile. "I'm sorry I didn't tell you, my dear, *ma chère*. He was taken away when you were very young, and we just didn't know. We didn't know if...well, if he would be coming back." Gabrielle looked up and pressed her fingers to her mouth, eyes shining with tears. There was nothing Gabrielle could say that would explain why her father was now standing at the front door. Gabrielle knelt down, put her arms around Chaya and repeated, "He is your Papa, Chaya. He has come all the way here to see you."

"No! He is my Papa!" Chaya cried, pointing to Gaston, and ran to him, wrapping her arms around his leg.

Chaya did not want anything to do with this somber, skeletal man. At less than 95 pounds, Zev was a frightening sight for a child. His sallow skin, sunken cheeks and hollowed eyes made him look like an old man, even though he was still in his thirties. Having just escaped from three years of hard labor and imprisonment, he hardly resembled the playful, adoring father he had been before the war.

Chaya was an infant the last time he'd seen her. Now she was already a girl. "I know you don't remember me, Chaya, but I remember you, even though you're much bigger now. And I can't tell you how happy I am to see you," said Zev, his voice hoarse with emotion.

Rivka stood behind Zev and repeated Gabrielle's words, "We have come to take you home with us."

A wave of panic rose from the pit of Chaya's belly. "Take me home?" she said.

Chaya looked at Gaston with pleading eyes, hoping he would say something, tell them he wouldn't let her go. Panic rose in her voice.

"But this is my home!" Tears streamed down Chaya's flushed cheeks.

Chaya ran to Gabrielle and clutched a handful of her skirt.

"Please Maman. I want to stay here!" she cried. "Don't make me go with them. Please!"

Gabrielle gazed down at Chaya, then at the stricken faces of Rivka and Zev.

"I would love more than anything for you to stay," Gabrielle whispered into Chaya's ear. "You know that. But there's nothing I can do." She took a deep breath to calm her nerves as she looked down, pretending to smooth her skirt. She patted Chaya's soft hand reassuringly.

"You are always welcome here, Chaya," said Gabrielle loud enough for Zev and Rivka to hear, "But they are your parents. You must do as they say."

Chaya looked at Rivka and Zev. She inched as far away from them as she could.

"I don't want to go with those people," she whispered weakly into Gabrielle's ear. "Please don't make me."

* * *

Zev was so spent, he could barely stand. He lowered himself into a chair like an old, withered man.

116

"I won't make you do anything, *ma chère*," said Gabrielle. "But for now, I think our visitors can use some food and rest right, yes? Let's go fix him something, shall we?" and offered her hand to Chaya.

Gaston brought Zev a pillow to sit on and wrapped a warm blanket around his shoulders.

"Thank you," he whispered, his voice hoarse and raspy.

Gabrielle went into the kitchen and returned carrying a tray with tea, a round of bread, sliced pears from their orchard, and fresh sheep's cheese with dill. She poured a cup of tea, added a drizzle of milk and a generous spoon of sugar and placed it in front of Zev. His hands shook as he lifted the cup. A stream of hot tea dripped onto his lap.

"I'm so sorry," he said, embarrassed, and placed the teacup back on its saucer. He steadied his hand and took another sip, savoring the soothing warmth of the tea.

It was the first time he had anything sweet in years, and it instantly lifted his spirits.

"Mmmm," he said, as swirls of steam warmed his face.

Zev's mind flashed back to the last time he had tea with Rivka—the very night he was thrown into the truck and taken away. He took in a deep breath and shook his head, trying to shake off this wretched memory.

He ate slowly, silently. So much had happened to them those past few years. So many unspeakable tragedies. Both his parents had been killed, along with most of his siblings, nieces, nephews, uncles, cousins. He had seen far more than most humans could bear. And yet he had miraculously survived.

I can hardly believe I'm sitting here, thought Zev, looking across at his beautiful daughter and wife, both with him again at last. He looked at the fresh plates of food, the sun streaming in, the sounds of farm animals, and the smell of freshly baked bread. It was a world away from the camps, a world he never thought he'd live to see again.

Zev's eyes brimmed with tears, suddenly overwhelmed. "Thank you. For everything," he said. He wanted to say more, express his gratitude for saving his daughter's life, but words failed him. These people had welcomed Chaya into their home, fed her, clothed her, and cared for her as if she were their own. He could tell the moment he walked in the door. And now they were generously welcoming him, too. He was little more than a stranger, and yet they treated him like family. "Chaya is like a daughter to us, so that makes you family, too," said Gaston, as though reading Zev's mind.

This act of kindness was almost too much for Zev, whose spirit was as diminished as his body. All he had known since that ill-fated night was the struggle for survival. He had been treated like a slave, an animal, a number. Zev looked at the tattoo etched into his forearm with pitch-black ink, forever marked as a prisoner of war.

"May I go lie down? I'm a bit tired," he asked, politely excusing himself from the table.

"Of course," said Gaston, and led him to Jilberte's room.

Jilberte rarely stayed at the house anymore, since her work demanded her to be at the hospital days in a row and the convent offered her student housing, both for safety and proximity. Jilberte's bed was piled with a goose down duvet that felt far too luxurious for Zev, having lived in bug-ridden barracks for so long. Lying on the bare, drafty floor felt safer, more familiar.

He tossed and turned, trying in vain to escape the nightmares that tormented him as he slept. The sounds of a tractor on a nearby farm turned into those of an army tank as he dreamt. A shrieking hawk became a child's cry. Heart racing, Zev woke up with a start. He looked around, disoriented.

Zev looked around, scanning the room: A stack of fresh towels rested on a low-lying stool. Atop the whitewashed dresser was a blue-and-white ceramic wash basin and a framed photograph of a child. He heard breathing and turned his head to see Rivka sleeping. Zev touched her hand. Without waking, she grasped his instinctively. Zev's heart rate slowed. *Yes, I am really here. And you are with me.* He took a deep breath, closed his eyes, and prayed for a dreamless night.

CHAPTER TWENTY-EIGHT

Bidding Farewell

Chaya, March 1945

Jilberte, Gabrielle and Gaston

While Zev relaxed after lunch, Gaston and Gabrielle sat in the garden and talked.

"You must stay with us, Rivka, at least until Zev is stronger," insisted Gabrielle. "He can barely function in his condition, let alone find a job."

"I know, Gabrielle," said Rivka. "It's just that you've done so much for us already."

"It'll be easier for Chaya, too," said Gaston. "She'll have some time to be with all of us, and it won't feel so rushed," he added kindly.

Within just a few weeks, Zev was already looking healthier. He kept busy helping Gaston out in the farm and enjoyed being out in the fresh air and open fields. He savored the view unspoiled by barbed wire fences, the sounds of nature unmarred by the harsh cries of German soldiers. For the first time in years, he wasn't a prisoner. The war was finally over.

Chaya shied away from her parents, preferring the warmth and familiar company of Gabrielle and Gaston, and her friend Madeleine. But when the time came to leave, Chaya did not fight or whine, but obediently went with her parents. There was no choice. Children listened to adults and did not argue. It was that simple.

"You can spend all your vacations with us," Gaston reassured Chaya.

Rivka had already agreed to this, to the Delfosse's great delight. "We will see you again soon, *mon petit chou*," and picked Chaya up to give her one last kiss and hug good-bye. Knowing that she would see her Maman and Papa again eased the pain of saying good-bye. But it left a hollow feeling in her belly and a tightness in her throat. Chaya clung to her tattered doll, Bébé, and followed Rivka and Zev down the dusty road, looking back towards her home until it became a little speck in the distance.

Chaya's parents did not talk to her along the way, nor hold her hand. They simply walked together, silently, toward the train station. She looked back one more time, hoping that Gaston would come running and refuse to let her go, but all she saw was a crowd of strangers.

* * *

"Three tickets for Brussels please," said Zev, as he handed the ticket agent correct change for the journey.

While he was recuperating, Gaston had helped Zev find an inexpensive two-bedroom apartment for rent in Brussels, and had also put him in touch with a builder who could give him some work.

"It's not much, but it'll help put a roof over your heads and food in your mouths," said Gaston humbly. Zev was grateful beyond words.

The apartment was simple but clean, with a clawfoot tub in the kitchen, hot and cold running water in the sink, electric lights, and a shared toilet down the hall. Zev and Rivka were glad to find the place sparsely furnished, with a mattress in each bedroom, a simple dining table, a sofa and a worn, tufted rug. All their furnishings were still back in Antwerp, now property of the Germans or whoever was living in their apartment. They were starting over again with little more than a half-filled suitcase, but at least they were out of hiding. With the war now over, they were finally free.

To help make ends meet, Zev rented the second bedroom to an American soldier named Joseph. Joe was tall and lanky, with a reddish-blond crew cut and freckles, which made him look like an overgrown boy.

"You can call me Joe," he said with an easy smile.

With all the barracks bombed, there was no place for soldiers to sleep unless they boarded with civilians.

Before leaving in the morning, Joe always made sure his bed was neatly made and his clothes stacked and folded. When Rivka commented on what a good "*balbusta*" he was, Joe said in a mixture of broken French and English, "That's what boot camp will do for ya. My sergeant was big into military corners—they had to be perfect every time, even though it was so dark when we woke up, we could hardly see. I had my share of latrine duty just learnin' how to make a bed."

When he came to breakfast the first morning of his stay, Joe confessed, "I broke the bedside lamp last night when I stretched out. Seems I'm longer than the bed," he smiled.

Joe was well over six-feet tall, and his bed was little more than a cot. "I'll replace it, Mr. Slomovich," he promised.

"Did you get hurt?" asked Zev. "Naw," said Joe, "I'm fine, sir."

"Then it's nothing to worry about," said Zev.

That night, Joe returned with a new lamp.

"It's not the same, but it's all I could find," he said.

Zev was amazed that with very few stores open, and little money to go around, that Joe had replaced the broken fixture.

"You are obviously a man of your word," said Zev, patting him on the shoulder.

When his six-month sojourn ended, Joe's officer notified him that he'd be returning to his post back in the United States.

"When you get to the States," Rivka asked, "Could you mail something for me?"

"Absolutely, ma'am. Just give me your letter and I'll send it as soon as I get there," said Joe.

The local post office was now little more than a pile of bricks, glass, and splintered wood. The one in the next town had not been bombed, but it had closed shortly after the war began, leaving little opportunity to send word to friends and family.

Rivka wrote to her cousin Eddie in New York and let him know that she, Zev, and Chaya were alive and well. While there was no guarantee the letter would ever reach Chaya's cousin, it was worth a try. Rivka tucked the letter in an envelope and handed it to Joe, and gave him some coins to pay for the postage.

When Joe left before dawn, he left a note of thanks, along with a chocolate bar for Chaya and his forwarding address back in the States. He left the coins for the postage, adding, *P.S. Belgian francs sure are pretty, but we can't use them back in the States. I'll take care of the stamp. Yours truly, Joe.*

CHAPTER TWENTY-NINE

Life in Brussels

Chaya, March 1946

Chaya

With the war over, Rivka and Zev now had to face the grim reality of all they'd lost. Gone were their parents, most of their siblings, and countless other relatives and friends. Gone were their childhood homes in Czechoslovakia, their flat in Antwerp, and most of their belongings. Gone was the world they knew.

As they struggled to reestablish their lives in Brussels, Rivka and Zev grew increasingly somber and inward. They rarely spoke and never laughed. Gone was the playful exuberance they possessed before the war. The traumas they'd endured had taken their toll, squeezing out the last remnants of joy. A dark veil seemed to hover over them, even on the sunniest days.

Chaya longed for the warm, loving home of her "other parents." She missed the comfort of Dowley, her friend Madeleine, and the barn cats, too. She had never felt more alone.

With Rivka and Zev, Chaya felt invisible. She was overshadowed by the ghosts of loved ones who had perished under Hitler's reign. There were too many tragedies, too much sorrow for lighthearted play or make-believe stories. Rivka and Zev had become so used to struggling to survive that they'd forgotten what it was like to simply be.

Chaya spent her time telling stories to Bébé and reading. Gaston had taught her to read when she was four, and books proved to be Chaya's closest companions. Jilberte had brought home a small parcel just before Chaya left—a package of three classic children's books in full color—and Chaya read them over and over again until she knew each page by heart.

When she turned five that January, Chaya was old enough to attend kindergarten. Most schools had been bombed, and the closest one still standing was a Catholic school run by devout nuns clad in full black habits. They were anything but warm and welcoming. Their tight, serious expressions, bat-like veils and heavy-heeled shoes made their presence even more foreboding. Chaya was terrified of them.

Chaya and her classmates lived in perpetual fear of being hit by the switch that rested on the teacher's desk like a viper, always ready to strike. Sometimes she simply held the stick like a pointer, tapping it in her palm as she recited addition tables.

"You don't want me to use this now, do you?" the nun would threaten when someone got an answer wrong. The fact that these students were less than six years old was besides the point.

At lunchtime, the cafeteria often served soup with strands of limp, overcooked celery. Stealthily, Chaya would extract the stringy bits from her soup and place them beneath her napkin, praying the nuns wouldn't see her. While she was never caught, it didn't stop Chaya from having dreams about the nuns making her eat potfuls of cooked celery as her punishment. Just thinking about the gooey greens made her queasy.

Eating breakfast on school days was difficult enough. Chaya's stomach tightened in anticipation of returning to school. On her daily walks, she grew more and more anxious as she approached the building, throwing up as the church's top spire came into view. This became a regular occurrence, so much so, that after awhile, Rivka simply brought a wet rag for cleanup.

Walking back after school was always much better. Rivka would meet Chaya after school and they would head home together. Chaya always felt a wave of relief, happy to be as far away from the stick-wielding nuns as possible. She escaped into the world of stories as soon as she arrived home.

On Sundays, Chaya took long walks with Zev, who enjoyed strolling around town and the bordering countryside. He loved the fresh air and wide open fields, and simply being with his daughter.

Whenever they passed a church, Chaya would run into it as Zev waited. Everything she knew about religion had come from Gabrielle and Gaston, and from school—all of which were Catholic. She knew little about her Jewish identity and even less about her parents' history.

"She doesn't need to know, at least not now," said Rivka on the rare occasions they discussed Chaya's religious upbringing. "What good will it do?"

"Did you know Chaya crosses herself every time we pass a church?" Zev asked Rivka.

"That's what she's been taught, Zev," said Rivka reassuredly. "She'll learn. It will just take some time."

Still, Rivka and Zev celebrated Shabbat every Friday, said prayers in Hebrew, and included Chaya while lighting the candles and eating fresh, braided challah. On Saturday morning, Zev quietly wrapped his tallit around his shoulders, placed a yarmulke on his head, and said the prayers he'd known by heart since he was a boy. Chaya simply watched, taking it all in. The ways of her parents felt foreign, strange. She looked forward to her next vacation, when she would finally be able to see the Delfosses again.

CHAPTER THIRTY

Dreaming of
America

Chaya, August 1947

Zev, Chaya and Rivka

Chaya spent holidays and school breaks back at the Delfosses, where life felt once again cheerful and relaxed.

"I wish I could just live here with you," she said to Gaston whenever she'd stay with them.

"You're always welcome," smiled Gaston, knowing all too well that they had no say over Chaya's visits—they were just happy to have her.

For the next two years, Chaya returned to the Delfosses as often as she could. While she was away, Rivka and Zev stayed busy working whatever odd jobs they could to earn enough money to pay for a voyage to America.

* * *

"You won't believe it, Rivka! It's finally come through!" announced Zev one afternoon, bursting through the front door flushed with excitement.

He held a piece of paper stamped with the word "APPROVED" in bold, bright red capital letters. Zev's sister, Pesel, now called "Pearl" in her new home of Los Angeles, California, had sponsored Zev and his family to come to America years earlier, but when the war broke out, everything was put on hold.

"We're going to America!" said Zev to Rivka, a big grin that brought his entire face to life.

Rivka opened her mouth in amazement and shock, then looked at Zev's beaming face and hugged him.

"I can't believe it," she said. "I can't believe it's actually happening."

She put her hand to her cheek, took in a deep breath, and sat down to absorb the news. Then she scanned the room, already thinking about what to pack for the overseas journey.

Zev and Rivka had heard the same rumors as everyone else—that America was "the land of milk and honey," that it was "paved with gold." They knew better than to believe everything they'd heard, but they did know that the United States was a place where people from anywhere in the world, rich or poor, could be free to build a new life. This was the place to go if they were to have any chance of starting over again.

* * *

Chaya, however, did not share her parents' excitement. When they broke the news that afternoon after school, she immediately broke into tears.

"Please, no! I don't want to go to America!" she cried. "I want to stay here with Maman and Papa!"

Zev's excitement drained, but Rivka was undeterred.

"We will only be gone two weeks," she said. "Then you can come back and live with them."

This seemed to calm Chaya down.

"Just two weeks, okay?" said Rivka again, wiping her tears.

"Okay," said Chaya quietly.

But when the day came to board the ship, Chaya refused.

"I don't want to go," she pleaded. "Please, Mother, I want to stay here."

They were holding up the line.

Panicked, Rivka made another promise, "If you get on the boat, I'll buy you a brand new bicycle, okay?"

While Chaya never asked for anything, one thing she wished for was a bike. She had never had one of her own, let alone one that was completely new.

Chaya took a hesitant step forward, then stopped, unconvinced.

"As soon as we get there, we'll get you a bicycle, okay? Then we'll bring it back here when we come back," said Rivka, taking her hand and leading the way.

With the bustle from the crowds propelling her forward, Chaya stepped onto the ship, promises of a shiny new bike and a life back with the Delfosses etched firmly in her mind.

CHAPTER THIRTY-ONE

A Stormy Voyage

Chaya, September 1947

The USS Oregon was an enormous ship by any measure, especially to a seven-year-old child who had never seen anything bigger than a sailboat. Standing from the port at Le Havre, France, Chaya found the ship both overwhelming and fascinating.

To her, the ship felt like a moving island, heading out towards the open sea. Built to withstand the elements, it offered little in the way of comfort. The decks were crowded with people speaking over one another like tangled yarns, trying to make themselves heard over the ocean winds. The railings were wet and slippery; the seating, worn and unforgiving.

The ship reminded Chaya of a giant sea dragon—a building-size beast with rows of beady porthole eyes that made loud, roaring sounds, and spewed angry bursts of steam. The port appeared to grow smaller and smaller, until it seemed to blur and then vanish. Among the throngs of adults, Chaya felt small, too, swallowed up by the floating dragon.

Rather than look around at the masses of people huddled around her, Chaya stared out at the water. It seemed to go on forever. She squinted her eyes to see just a bit farther, but all she could make out was a flat horizon. Waves splashed the side of the ship, misting them with sea water. It tasted salty, leaving her skin moist and sticky.

As the ship backed out from the port, Chaya looked toward the land and thought about being back with the Delfosses. *Just two weeks and I'll be back.* This promise comforted her as the ship rocked back and forth, pitching her small body forward. As she fell, Zev grabbed her arm and brought her close. Then he took her hand, leaned over, and gently kissed the top of her head. Rivka looked at Chaya and Zev and smiled, then gave Chaya's shoulders a gentle squeeze.

"We're on our way," said Rivka, as the ship slowly, carefully backed out of the port.

Having never learned how to swim, Chaya was terrified of falling in the water, but she was also fascinated by it—the way it swirled around the ship and swelled into waves, its color changing from muddy green to navy blue and turquoise as they moved into the open sea.

While the chilling wind cut right through their layers of clothing, the warmth of the sun made the first few days tolerable. Then, like a curtain closing, the sky filled with storm clouds, creating a thick gray veil that darkened everything below it. Seagulls hovered overhead, making shrieking sounds as they frantically looked for shelter. The water looked nearly black, its frothy foam swirling around like witch's brew.

"All passengers must come inside," announced the captain from a loudspeaker in French. "Please take your seats, *madames et messieurs. Merci.*"

The ship's captain was aware of a brewing storm, but hadn't anticipated how turbulent it would be. Within minutes, a deluge of rain fell from the sky, as though the ocean had righted itself. Thunder and lightning struck, illuminating the water in flickers and bursts. Waves rocked the ship as though it was a bathtub toy, swaying the huddled passengers from side to side. A few people were lucky enough to find lifesavers and held on tight, while others simply grasped onto the rims of the slippery benches.

Chaya closed her eyes, trying to wish the scene away, or at least sleep through it. But all it did was add to her queasiness. Within the hour, she experienced her first bout of seasickness. Rivka held Chaya's hair back as she wretched into a bucket.

The storm went from bad to worse, turning into a full-fledged hurricane. At night, the ship rocked so violently, Chaya fell out of the top bunk while she was sleeping. To her great surprise, she landed on her feet, and dreamt she had flown. Only when she was fully awake, did she realize the extent of the ship's sway and ran to the sink, where she was once again sick.

Unable to keep much down from constant seasickness, Chaya became drawn and lethargic. She dared not eat, in fear of it coming back up, but Rivka did what she could to keep Chaya hydrated.

"Here," said Rivka, handing Chaya a cloth soaked in cool water, "Suck on this. It will help keep your mouth wet."

Food became more and more scarce as the days progressed, but with the ship's constant rocking, most of the passengers felt too seasick to think about eating much. They simply prayed for the storm to abate and the sight of dry land.

CHAPTER THIRTY-TWO

WELCOME TO AMERICA

Chaya, October 1947

Rivka, Chaya and Zev

On October 7, 1947, after eleven seemingly endless days and nights, the ship neared Ellis Island. The waters had finally settled, and rays of sunlight poked through the billowy clouds. Chaya's face flushed for the first time in days as she caught sight of the Statue of Liberty. "Mother, look!" she said, gazing up at the giant statue. "She's as tall as the sky!" "She certainly is one big lady," smiled Zev, gazing up in awe.

The passengers began to crowd together again as they neared the port to Ellis Island. Overwhelmed and exhausted, Chaya's temperature began to rise.

"It's so hot," she said, trying to take off her coat. "It's freezing out here, *mamela*" said Rivka. "You have to keep your coat on."

"But I'm so hot," said Chaya, as droplets of sweat gathered on her forehead.

Rivka held her hand to Chaya's face. She had definitely spiked a fever.

"They'll put us in quarantine if they find out Chaya's sick," whispered Rivka to Zev, clearly worried.

As they gathered their things, a nun approached them. Her smiling eyes and kind expression made her far less frightening to Chaya than the blanched, poker-faced nuns she had known back in Belgium.

"Here," she said quietly to Rivka, "Some baby aspirin for your little girl. They taste like chalk, but at least she'll be able to chew them. It will help take away the fever."

She handed two small powdery pills to Rivka.

"Thank you so much," said Rivka.

"Take these," said Rivka to Chaya. "They'll help you feel better."

Too weary to protest, Chaya did as she was told. Within the hour, her fever broke, and she was already beginning to feel better. Still, the crowds overwhelmed her. She'd never seen so many people in one place in all her life.

Rivka, Zev and Chaya stood in one line after another, answering what seemed to be an endless stream of questions about their country of origin, their sponsor, their family, their destination.

But the first question was the most jarring of all: "Name?" asked one officer to Rivka.

"Rivka Slomovich," she responded. The officer wrote down her name: Ruth Salomon. Rivka tried to correct the officer, but he simply stamped her passport and yelled, "Next!" to keep the endless line moving along.

Chaya looked at her family's new American names. The name Helen was written on her passport; the name William on her father's. She looked up at her parents, wondering why the man couldn't get their names right. Still, she kept quiet. She'd learned long ago to keep her thoughts to herself.

Chaya looked around at all the people mulling about, expecting them to look more like the American characters she had read about storybooks, but they didn't seem much different from the folks she'd seen back in Belgium.

"Where are all the cowboys and Indians?" she whispered to her parents, still on the lookout. Zev chuckled.

"I haven't spotted any yet, but I'll let you know if I do," he whispered back.

Exhausted from their journey, Chaya, Zev, and Rivka sat together outside, relishing the fresh air and sunshine. It felt wonderful to be back on solid ground.

"I still feel like I'm on the boat," said Chaya, walking like a drunken sailor across the grass.

"You'll get your land legs back in another day or so," smiled Rivka.

Zev bought a soft pretzel from a street vendor and split it among them.

Chaya picked off the salt before biting into the warm, squishy dough.

"Look! The ground sparkles," she said, noticing the glint of crystals reflecting off the sidewalk.

"Are there diamonds in there?" she asked.

"No," said Zev, smiling, "But I have heard that America is paved with gold—and maybe diamonds, too," he said, and gave her a wink.

Chaya marveled at how different America seemed. Everything seemed to shine like a brand new coin. Back home, she had gotten used to seeing piles of rubble, boarded up and abandoned buildings. For the first time, there were no tanks or army trucks in sight, no rockets whistling or rifles firing. The only sounds were those of people, birds, and the sea.

Nestled between her parents, Chaya sat on a park bench watching two children flying paper kites. When the wind died down, they put the kites on the grass and played a game of chase, giggling as they ran. Chaya smiled as she watched them.

"You want to go play?" asked Rivka.

"No," Chaya smiled. "I just want to stay here with you."

Rivka and Zev looked at one another, then without a word, each took Chaya's hand. Together, they sat on the bench, basking in the sun, the fresh air, and their first taste of freedom.

Chaya, 1947

EPILOGUE

Despite the fact that they didn't speak the language, didn't have a home, or much of anything beyond what they carried in their suitcases, Rivka and Zev remained hopeful. After all, "America was there for the taking, as long as you were willing to work for it," they were told time and again—and both of them were willing and able.

For the first two months, Rivka, Zev, and Chaya stayed with relatives in New York, then New Jersey and Ohio before riding a train to California. It took three days to cross the country. There, they stayed with Zev's sister Pearl before finding an apartment for themselves.

It didn't take Chaya long to realize she wasn't going back to Belgium. Weeks passed, then months, with no sign they were returning. Asking was of no use. Chaya's parents were too busy trying to start a new life in the U.S. Her father spent long days laboring at a record factory, while her mother worked with a neighbor as a seamstress.

Chaya did get a bicycle, a shiny pink-and-white two-wheeler with a bell, training wheels, and a special tin bucket that hung from the handlebars. She cherished this bike and wished she could show Gaston that she could ride all on her own.

The biggest surprise came nearly two years later, when Chaya's baby sister, Raizel, was born. She called her sister Bébé and was as nurturing as any *petite maman* could be. "You are my little helper," said Rivka time and again as she watched Chaya lift her from her crib, feed Raizel a bottle, and read her fairy tales.

When Raizel was nearly a year old, they headed back to Ohio, where Rivka's brother, Meyer and sisters, Toby and Chaiju, had immigrated from Czechoslovakia. They were the only surviving members of her once large family. Meyer had begun to make a name for himself as a contractor and offered Zev a job, which would offer a much better living than his job back at the record factory in California.

All the while, Chaya kept writing to the Delfosse family. It didn't take long for her to realize that she would never live with her Maman and Papa again, but her dream of seeing them again never waned. She wrote to them throughout elementary school, high school, and college. She shared news of her marriage and of her teaching career, the birth of her children and her grandchildren.

Chaya kept in touch with the Delfosse family her entire childhood, adolescence and adulthood, but did not have the opportunity to return there until 1987, when she was nearly 50 years old. She never saw Gaston again. He had survived cancer, but died of pneumonia in 1961 when Chaya was a junior at Oberlin College.

Gabrielle died in 1989 at the age of 89. Jilberte worked as a midwife for many years. She never married. Now in her early 90s, she lives just a few miles from her childhood home.

Zev lived long enough to fulfill the wish that kept him going during the war—to see Chaya married, but died of a sudden heart attack the day after Thanksgiving in 1962, just four months after Chaya's wedding. Zev had just turned 51.

For the next 40 years, Rivka supported herself as a seamstress in her home in Cleveland, and played a large part in the lives of her grandchildren and great-grandchildren, all of whom regarded her as not only a generous and loving grandmother, but also true hero. She worked until she was 87 years old and died when she was nearly 92.

Chaya is now in her mid-70s, living in a house built by her Uncle Meyer more than 40 years ago. She is a wife, a mother, and a grandmother.

Most people who lived through the Holocaust are long gone. Since she was just an infant during the war, Chaya is among the youngest survivors of this era. More than 1.5 million children perished.

Over 25,000 women and children were sent from Malines to Auschwitz, never to return. Chaya may very well be the only infant to survive this internment camp. We can only hope there were others, but we may never know.

Over the years I've wondered why I survived while so many others did not.
Does the answer lie with my children? My grandchildren?
It's a comforting thought, but I really don't know.
What I do know is that I survived so I can speak about it.
And so I am.

A WORD FROM THE AUTHOR

This is a book about my mother, Helen (Salomon) Marks. Rather than use her Yiddish name, Henya, I chose the name Chaya because of its meaning ("life"). While writing this story, I learned that Chaya was also the name of my great-great grandmother, which makes it all the more special.

My mother, a gifted wordsmith and historian, spent many hours relaying her memories, as well as accounts she'd heard from her parents and relatives through the years. Her experiences and those of my grandmother are the focus of this book.

I have countless memories of sitting around my grandmother's kitchen table, listening with rapt attention to her experiences in the Holocaust, and they obviously made a lasting impression on me. As a mother, Rivka didn't dwell as much on her past, since she was more focused on simply surviving and raising her kids. But when she became a grandmother, however, her memories came flooding back. I am grateful that my grandmother felt comfortable sharing her stories, and that I can now share them with you.

Rivka came close to death many times, but somehow managed to survive. A combination of luck, serendipity, and the kindness of strangers is what ultimately saved her and my mother. If it wasn't for the Delfosse family, my mother would probably not be alive today, nor would I be here telling you this story.

GLOSSARY

balbusta *(Yiddish)*: term for a good housekeeper, someone who does a good job around the house (cooking, cleaning, etc.)

bébé *(French)*: baby

bubela *(Yiddish)*: term of endearment used toward someone (often grand-mothers to children) considered darling and close to one's heart

gehen *(German)*: plural form of the verb "to go," meaning "we go"

hamotze *(Yiddish/Hebrew)*: Jewish blessing over bread

keneinahora *(Yiddish)*: superstitious saying, said to ward away the "evil eye"

kibbitzing *(Yiddish)*: chatting

kugel *(Yiddish)*: Eastern European potato casserole

gestapo *(German)*: the official secret police of Nazi German and German-occupied Europe

mamela *(Yiddish)*: little girl, little mother

ma petite chou *(French)*: my little cabbage, term of endearment

matzoh *(Hebrew/English)*: flat, unleavened bread traditionally eaten by Jews during Passover

mein shaine maideleh *(Yiddish)*: my pretty girl

mijn god *(Flemish)*/ **mon dieu** *(French)*: exclamatory expression, meaning "my God"

Mourner's Kaddish: Hebrew prayer said in honor of those who have died

petite maman *(French)*: little mother

quelle surprise *(French)*: what a surprise

shmatah *(Yiddish)*: rag

swastika *(German)*: symbol associated with the Nazi party

tallit *(Hebrew)*: shawl with fringes worn over the head and shoulders of Jewish males during religious services

yarmulke *(Hebrew)*: a small, round skullcap traditonally worn by religious Jewish men and boys

Rivka and Chaya, photographed by Carl Hensler

Chaya and Rivka in Belgium, 1946

Gabrielle and Jilberte in Blankenberg, Belgium

Zev (Bill) and Raizel (Rosiland)

*Wedding of Helen Salomon (Chaya) to
Robert Marks, July 1, 1962*

Salomon family in Los Angeles, 1949

Jilberte and Helen (Chaya), July 2013

The Delfosse's farmhouse, photographed in July 2013

Image of the hill Chaya and her friend Madeleine used to roll down together

Made in the USA
Columbia, SC
06 September 2021